629

W9-CPE-076

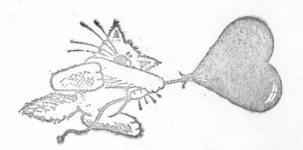

by Martin Caidin

THE ASTRONAUTS

AVIATION AND SPACE
  MEDICINE
    with Grace Caidin

BLACK THURSDAY

BY APOLLO TO THE
  MOON

CROSS-COUNTRY
  FLYING

EVERYTHING BUT THE
  FLAK

GOLDEN WINGS

I AM EAGLE!
  with Gherman Titov

IT'S FUN TO FLY

LET'S GO FLYING

THE LONG ARM OF
  AMERICA

THE LONG LONELY
  LEAP
    *with Capt. J. W. Kittin-
    ger, Jr.*

THE MAN-IN-SPACE
  DICTIONARY

THE MIGHTY
  HERCULES

THE MOON: NEW
  WORLD FOR MEN

THE NIGHT HAMBURG
  DIED

OVERTURE TO SPACE

RED STAR IN SPACE

RENDEZVOUS IN SPACE

THE SILKEN ANGELS

SPACEPORT U.S.A.

TEST PILOT

THIS IS MY LAND

THUNDERBIRDS!

A TORCH TO THE
  ENEMY

WAR FOR THE MOON

FLYING

ZERO!
  *with Masatake Okumiya
  and Jiro Horikoshi*

THE
MIGHTY
HERCULES

A KC-130F Hercules refuels a Cougar reconnaissance jet fighter high over the earth. (*U.S. Navy*)

THE
MIGHTY
HERCULES

by MARTIN CAIDIN

Illustrated with photographs

E. P. DUTTON & CO., INC. NEW YORK

This book is for
HANK CURTH

PREFACE

THE STRIP is barely two thousand feet long. It is a tiny clearing set in the midst of wild jungle country. All around the strip there are steep hills, their sides choked with trees, bamboo, and thick undergrowth. It is wild country through which men can struggle only with difficulty.

The tiny clearing is the only hope left for eight hundred men. The jungle all about them conceals thousands of Communist guerrillas. This is Southeast Asia, and many men here are fighting a deadly "shadow war" in the jungle lands.

The guerrillas greatly outnumber the small force at the clearing. They have pushed them back steadily until they are surrounded. The defenders have set up positions for a half-mile around the clearing. There can be no help from a rescuing force, and there is no way out through the jungle. On all sides there are the thickly covered hills and the guerrillas lurking in the growth.

7

Of the eight hundred trapped men, at least half are wounded. They are low on food, water, medical supplies, and even ammunition. Their situation seems desperate.

But now they have a chance. For two days and nights they have been hacking the clearing. Each day they have received some supplies by paradrops. Small transports raced over at low level and hurled packages of ammunition, food, and medicine to them.

During the day, fighter bombers have come to their aid. The single- and twin-engine airplanes roared low over the jungles. Whenever they found a sign of the guerrillas, they hurled tanks of napalm into the jungle. From the trees there leaped huge roaring tongues of fire. The planes dropped bombs, and strafed with machine guns and cannon.

The one chance the eight hundred men have is to be flown out. Transport airplanes into which many men could be packed must be able to land in that tiny clearing. The task seems impossible. A small liaison airplane could hardly get in and out of that single rough strip.

Early one morning, a great four-engine transport came into sight. Its wings gleamed silver in the sun, and its engines throbbed deeply. As guerrillas trained their guns on the big airplane, fighter bombers raced up and down, bombing and strafing.

At the rear of the transport, a wide ramp extended downward. The entire fuselage of the airplane came into view. Slowing down to 150 miles per hour, its crew ignoring the bullets that spattered into the body of the airplane, the transport droned directly over the jungle clearing.

A parachute blossomed suddenly from the open ramp. It whipped back into the air, trailing a long cable. Then a bulky object fell into the air. Giant folds of nylon unfurled, blossoming into parachutes. They lowered the cargo safely at one end of the clearing.

As men swarmed over the cargo, the transport came back a second time, and again the parachutes blossomed into the sky. A second load dropped earthward.

On the ground, men stripped away restraining cables and chains. Seconds later a motor roared into life, and one man drove off in a bulldozer! Soon afterward, the second bulldozer was thundering along the clearing. Working steadily, the two bulldozers flattened and scraped along the ground. Stones and bushes were shoved out of the way, trenches filled, and mounds graded level.

Many hours later, when the bulldozer engines fell silent, the men had scraped out a crude strip two thousand feet long, but few pilots would want to land here. It might be tried in a very light liaison airplane with one engine, or in a helicopter. But never in a big transport.

The next morning, as light swept over the earth, a Hercules transport appeared in the distance. It was many thousands of feet above the ground. Still high

up, the airplane slowed in flight. The landing gear
dropped down, huge flaps were lowered from the wings,
and the engines increased their snarl of power. The
Hercules headed for the airstrip, and then—fell out of
the sky.

The Hercules falls like a great wounded creature,
plunging for that rough, short strip. A wing scrapes
past a hill, perilously close. On each side of the big
airplane, fighters streak over the trees, firing all their
weapons to keep the guerrillas under cover.

The Hercules slams into the ground with terrific
force. It doesn't land—it crashes into the field. The
wings seem to flap crazily as they bend far down,
then spring up again. The airplane rocks and careens
wildly. Instantly dust springs up in a choking cloud,
swirling around the great metal shape. Then from the
dust there comes an ear-splitting howl. The dust cloud
plunges along the strip. Through the dust it is possible to see flashes of metal. Then, less than a thousand
feet from where it struck the earth, the airplane slams
to a stop.

One of the men watching cries out: "He's crashed!"

He stares in disbelief as the "crashed airplane" suddenly comes to life with a burst of power from its engines. It tilts crazily to one side as the pilot rams it
around in a turn, and heads back for the other end of
the strip. Then it turns once more, pointing down the
strip.

The entire rear of the airplane is lowered to form a

ramp. As men with guns stand watchfully about the airplane, other men move quickly onto the ramp. They are carrying wounded men on stretchers. Other wounded men are helped aboard into the gaping fuselage.

Minutes later the ramp comes up and seals the rear of the airplane. The pilot talks crisply into his radio. Then he looks through the windows as fighters scream down, blasting at guerrilla positions in the jungle.

At that moment, the pilot rams the throttles all the way forward. The airplane that "crashed" rushes down the strip. The pounding underneath the airplane is fierce. The gear hammers and bangs from the rough surface. But long before the end of the strip is reached, the great transport is soaring at a steep angle into the air.

Even as it rushes for altitude, a second silver shape is falling out of the sky. Another Hercules is on its way down for an impossible "crash landing."

Two hours later, the Communist guerrillas walk across the clearing. Not one of the eight hundred men is there.

The Hercules had come.

CONTENTS

PREFACE 7

1 KEY TO GREATNESS 15

2 MEET THE HERCULES 23

3 TO DO THE JOB 39

4 THE BIG PUSH 61

5 IN THE COCKPIT 83

6 ASSAULT! 94

7 STRIKE! 105

8 MISSION TO EUROPE 129

9 THE AMAZING HERCULES 144

10 THE TWO-EDGED SWORD 155

11 KALEIDOSCOPE 161

A bulldozer floats gently to earth beneath a spread of six parachutes after being air-dropped from a Hercules. (*U.S. Army*)

KEY TO GREATNESS

THROUGHOUT the history of aviation, engineers have designed many hundreds of different types of airplanes. These have included everything from small flyweight models carrying only one man to giants that weigh nearly 500,000 pounds. There have been trainers, fighters, transports, flying boats, airliners, crop-dusters, bombers, research craft, private and business airplanes, aerobatic ships, amphibians, firefighters, and dozens of other types.

But to the men who fly there are only *two* types of airplanes. There are many of the first category, but only a few of the second. Almost all airplanes built are "ordinary" machines. They are the first type. They fly; they do their job, and sometimes they even do it especially well. But they are just airplanes.

And then there is the second type. These are the aircraft that pilots consider destined for greatness. They are among the small minority of airplanes that belong forever in aviation's hall of fame.

An airplane may become one of the all-time greats

for any one of a hundred reasons—or for many of those reasons. It is impossible to tell before an airplane enters service just what its career will be. No one knows what will happen when pilots are forced to exceed safety margins and to take impossible chances. But when that very special "something" happens—why, every man who ever took to the sky knows that another "immortal" has been born.

One of the greatest of all the airplanes is the famed Douglas DC-3. It is known by a bewildering variety of designations. To the commercial airlines of the world, which still fly the twin-engined airliners by the thousands, it is the DC-3. To the Air Force, the DC-3 in military colors has been officially classified as the C-39, C-47, C-48, C-49, C-50, C-51, C-52, C-53, and the C-117!

Each model was designed to perform a different mission, but the Air Force discovered that the basic C-47 cargo carrier could be adapted to almost any task it demanded. Thus the most famous of all the Air Force models became the C-47 Skytrain.

However, if you ask an Air Force pilot about the Skytrain, most likely he won't even know what you're talking about. To the men who flew the C-47, it was simply the Gooney Bird.

The Navy designated their C-47 models as the R4D, and sent them into service all over the world. They used their Gooney Birds in seven different versions, and after World War II, added the R4D-8. It is still the Gooney Bird, but it is not the same airplane. It is

a souped-up model, with more powerful engines,
stronger wings and body, and a high, sweeping tail.
In civilian life it is the Super DC-3.

The British bought hundreds of C-47's and promptly
named them Dakotas. No one paid much attention to
the British title, and even the Royal Air Force C-47's
finally became accepted as the Gooney.

The Gooney Bird isn't much of an airplane to look
at. It first flew in 1935, and it had two engines, each
of 1,200 horsepower. The Gooney Birds flying today
have the same engines, the same propellers, and their
performance has changed hardly at all. Thus, it is all
the more amazing that so many of these airplanes are
still in service, and still in demand.

The Russians copied the Gooney, called it the Ilush-
yin IL-2, and built them by the hundreds. They even
mounted a turret with a machine gun atop their red-
starred Gooneys, and sent them into battle in World
War II. It worked so well that they put two more machine guns into the fuselage, one on each side, and
sent the planes back into the battle.

Strictly on their own, several of our C-47 crews did
the same thing. They mounted .50-caliber machine
guns in the fuselage. When Japanese Zero fighters
roared in to attack the unarmed and helpless transport
they were greeted with blasts of machine-gun fire.

American fighter planes in World War II even shot
down several Gooney Birds. Not by accident, either—
but deliberately. These Gooneys, however, were exact
copies of our own airplane—and built by the Japanese,

whose pilots considered it their best transport plane.

So in the Gooney Bird we have one of the truly immortal planes. It has been flying for nearly thirty years.
More than twelve thousand were built. It is an airplane
that carried passengers and mail, that fought storms
and blizzards, years before many of the pilots flying
it today were even born.

It is the only airplane the United States Government
has declared to be certified for passenger operations
"just as long as the airplane is fit for flight."

Why did the Gooney Bird achieve its unmatched
fame? After all, it is a small airplane. It was never
the fastest airliner or transport, never the largest, and
it never had the greatest range. It couldn't fly the
highest, or carry the heaviest loads. Other airplanes
could outfly the Gooney Bird in many different ways.

But none of them could do so many different things.
None of them were so easy and gentle to fly, so sure
on the controls, so forgiving of mistakes. You could
beat a Gooney until it was battered and worn, and still
it could fly. You could pile cargo and people into a
Gooney until it was so overloaded the tires were almost
mashed flat. Engineers studied the sagging airplane
and said it could not fly. But no one could convince
the pilot, who took the airplane into the air.

You could drop the Gooney into rough dirt fields
that were simply too short for the airplane. The engineers said that it couldn't be landed safely in the
fields. And again the pilots refused to listen, and did
the impossible.

That was the key to it. The Gooney Bird defied the rules of flight. It seemed to sneer at the laws of engineering, and to ignore the fears of its passengers. And it ran and ran. When the mechanics didn't have tools or spare parts, they patched the airplane with wire and masking tape. When the parts were badly battered and bent, they slammed them back into shape with hammers. The airplane continued to fly.

Recently an Air Force major who has more than ten thousand hours of flying time in the Gooney Bird made his first flight at the controls of a powerful new transport.

It was a big, rugged airplane, built by the Lockheed-Georgia Company of Marietta, Georgia. The Air Force knows it as the C-130 Hercules, and it differs greatly from the old Gooney.

Its wing extends outward from the top of the fuselage, rather than from the bottom. It has four slim engines instead of the two thick and short engines of the C-47.

It didn't perform like the Gooney Bird, either. For one thing, the C-47 weighed 29,000 pounds. The Hercules into which the major climbed weighed, for this particular takeoff, 132,000 pounds. The old Gooney could get off the ground in an emergency takeoff in just about 2,000 feet, and this was tight. So the major, quite naturally, expected a long takeoff run with the Hercules. After all, the airplane weighed 103,000 pounds more than the Gooney. In fact, it weighed nearly as much as five C-47 transports combined.

The major wasn't at all prepared for what happened. He sat in the right seat (copilot seat) of the flight deck. That in itself amazed him. The cockpit of the C-47 was a small, restricted space into which two seats were squeezed. But the Hercules . . . well, there were four large, comfortable seats; there were two large bunks, and there was plenty of walking space. So it wasn't a cockpit at all; it was a flight deck.

When the major ran the engines in the Gooney Bird to full power just before takeoff, the two engines howled and thundered with energy. The roar was deafening, and sound waves crashed against the airplane.

Now, even with four engines and those big propellers, the sound in the Hercules' flight deck wasn't even uncomfortable. The major was more convinced than ever that the Hercules would roll for many thousands of feet before it could get into the air.

The pilot turned to him. "Would you like us to do an assault takeoff?" he asked.

What was an "assault takeoff"? He had never heard of it. However, why not? "Sure," he replied, "let's see what it's like."

The Hercules pilot grinned at him. His right hand grasped the power levers and slowly moved them forward. Slowly but steadily the big transport began to vibrate and shake. As the power came to its maximum level, the Hercules vibrated like a tree in a windstorm.

"Okay! Get your head full back against the headrest," the pilot warned. The major moved his head back an inch.

"No—not enough," the Hercules pilot warned. "Get it snug, well against the headrest."

The older pilot shrugged and pressed his head back. The young pilot of the Hercules nodded and said, "All right—we'll get going now."

With the word "now" he snapped the brakes free. The giant airplane shot forward with a tremendous jolt. It burst away from its standing position on the runway as though it were being shot out of a gun. The major couldn't believe it; the force of the takeoff was so great his body was shoved hard back against his seat.

The runway flashed by the side windows. The acceleration of the airplane was incredible.

Twelve seconds after releasing the brakes, the Hercules pilot pulled back on the control yoke. He didn't ease it back as pilots normally do with big airplanes. He hauled it back toward him.

In the right seat the major almost shouted. It was too soon. They had moved less than 1,200 feet down the runway—they'd never get into the air!

His jaw dropped in astonishment. The Hercules lifted its nose higher and higher. After moving for only 1,200 feet down the runway it leaped from the ground. The pilot held the nose up at its steep angle. Engines and propellers throbbing, the Hercules clawed its way into the sky at more than 2,000 feet per minute.

It kept right on climbing until, less than 14 minutes later, the pilot leveled off the airplane at an altitude of 26,000 feet. The major was dumbfounded. In those

14 minutes the Hercules had soared to an altitude that was greater than the old C-47 could even reach.

As the airplane remained in level flight, the speed built up. The Hercules pilot adjusted the power and fuel controls, and settled back to relax. From the right seat the major stared at the instruments. He muttered: "I see it—but I still don't believe it!"

The giant airplane was cruising at a speed of 340 miles per hour. This was astounding. The Hercules had taken off in just about half the distance required for the rugged twin-engine transport. And it was cruising higher than the Gooney could fly at more than twice the speed.

Much later, when the Hercules pilot had demonstrated the full performance of the four-engined assault transport, the airplane returned to the ground. The major climbed out of the flight deck and walked around to the front of the Hercules. Then he turned to the pilot of the big airplane.

"You know," he said, "I've just thought of something. This airplane is going to be the Gooney Bird of the 1970's."

The Hercules pilot laughed. "You may be right," he said, "but we think of the airplane in a different way. To us, the Hercules is the Gooney Bird of the jet age."

And that's about the nicest compliment that any airplane could ever receive.

MEET THE HERCULES 2

THE MODERN airplane is a beautiful and sleek symbol of the jet age. The graceful giants that flash through the skies are famed for their wings swept sharply back. We think of a fuselage as long and slender, of a tail that soars high and graceful above the ground. It is streamlining carried to the nth degree.

The Hercules is the most rugged, best-performing, and reliable airplane of its type ever built. It can do things no other airplane can and it does them all the time, as part of its normal mission.

But the Hercules simply does not fit our ideas of the sleek lines that represent the jet age.

It is squat, square, and massive. The wing juts out from atop the fuselage. There are very few big airplanes built this way any more. The only streamlining is in the bulletlike nacelles that house the four Allison jet engines. But even they seem strange, for at the end of each jet engine is a great, fat-bladed propeller.

The basic design of the Hercules is a radical departure from that of most airplanes. Jet engines mean

23

great speed and the sleekest lines. The Hercules is a mixture of the old and the new. It uses the jet engine but retains the propeller. When the Hercules first flew in 1954 it was the first airplane in the country to go into production as a turboprop. This is the jet engine linked with the propeller.

The shape of its nose is enough to make a designer break down and weep. There is very little that is modern or streamlined about it. The front end of the Hercules is a great expanse of metal and glass, and from it extends a black, bulbous shape that houses complex electronic equipment and radar antenna.

Within the flight deck the two pilots and the flight engineer scan one radarscope, and the navigator a second scope. They can switch to different power set-

One of the first Hercules transports to roll off the production line—an early model of the "squat, square, and rugged" giant. (*Lockheed-Georgia*)

tings and ranges. They can use that radar to outline the exact shape of coast lines, rivers, and mountains. Even if they are flying over a thick belt of clouds, or even at night, the radar gives them electronic vision.

But that is not all it does. By switching to the weather mode of the radar, they can fly safely through the most violent storms. Inside the black housing, a dish-shaped antenna whirls and flicks back and forth at great speed, sending out invisible beams of energy. When these reflect back at different frequencies, they act as weather eyes for the crew. They can tell when there's rain ahead, when the air is turbulent or when there's lightning. Being able to see in this electronic fashion, even in the middle of a storm at night, they can thread their way through the worst of the storm in complete safety.

Atop the radome that bulges from the nose of the airplane are the flight-deck windows, providing excellent visibility.

The belly of the airplane seems almost to scrape the concrete of the flight line. You can't see any of the gear legs for the tires. From each side of the fuselage, about midway between the fat nose and the towering tail, there extend two huge bulges. These are the special pods for the landing gear. The airplane seems to rest more on caterpillar treads than it does on wheels.

The fuselage is almost unbelievable. Airplanes are designed to present the cleanest shape to the winds in high-speed flight. The fuselage of the Hercules seems to bulge, from the beginning of the airplane almost all the way back to the tail.

From the top to the bottom of its huge body, the Hercules measures more than thirteen feet, and from side to side the distance is more than fourteen feet. The airplane itself is almost one hundred feet long, and most of this is made up of the hulking fuselage. Then comes the huge tail, slanting upward from the airplane to more than thirty-eight feet above the concrete ramp.

After studying this massive shape, it is hard to believe that the graceful and sweeping wings belong to the same airplane. It does not seem possible that the wing, which stretches just a little more than 132 feet from tip to tip, could drag this monster through the air.

The Hercules was designed to meet an Air Force requirement for a turboprop-powered, long-range transport that could carry cargo at high speed. The weight of cargo was not the only factor to be considered. Just as important was the airplane's ability to handle bulky loads, such as huge crates or massive machines. The Hercules had to be able to pick up tremendous loads and fly them to their destination. This is why the airplane has a great, wide, and deep fuselage.

But the Air Force also wanted an airplane to carry passengers as well as cargo. Sometimes it would have to transport both cargo and passengers. This complicated the design requirements. Since the airplane flew at high altitudes—up to eight miles above the earth—

the passengers and the crew would need both oxygen and pressurization.

It is easy to seal off and pressurize the crew compartment. But to do this for the huge volume of the Hercules' fuselage was a staggering problem. The engineers worked long and hard, and developed one of the most outstanding airplane pressure systems ever built.

The cargo compartment of the C-130B is 41.4 feet long, 10 feet wide and 9.1 feet high. Cargo loaded aboard the airplane can fit into a usable volume of

Crewman load a tank into the gaping rear hatch of the Hercules. After a flight of 2,000 miles to a combat area, the tank will be air-dropped and lowered by parachutes. (*U.S. Air Force*)

4,300 cubic feet. But there is a greater volume inside the airplane than this. There are the flight deck, passageways, and areas atop the airplane near the ceiling of the fuselage.

Despite all this space, the entire fuselage is pressurized and air-conditioned. When the Hercules flies at 35,000 feet, the pressure inside the fuselage is equal to that at 8,000 feet above sea level. There is always the possibility that some passenger might need 100 per cent oxygen. The airplane has more than 100 outlets for this purpose. The Hercules is one of the few airplanes that is ready at all times to operate an iron lung.

The air-conditioning system is a blessing to the crews and passengers when they fly to desert and jungle areas. Even on the ground it is possible to seal off and cool the Hercules. This is not done only for comfort. When another airplane stays on the ground for several hours in equatorial or desert regions it becomes so hot that a man could easily fall unconscious while doing strenuous work.

Then, there's the matter of delicate or fragile cargo. The Hercules' air-conditioning system provides cool air on the ground and warm air at high altitude (where it is sometimes 90° below zero), and so the cargo can be kept at the best temperature.

It is not always possible to see the secret ingredients of an airplane design just by looking at it. Many engineers take care to observe Murphy's Law, that states:

What Can Go Wrong, WILL Go Wrong. If there is even a possibility of failure or danger, they will eliminate that feature of the design. That the Hercules is fully pressurized could easily constitute a grave danger.

Any big, pressurized fuselage may suffer an explosive decompression. Something may pierce the side of the fuselage. If the airplane has a pressure of 8,000 feet inside, and is flying at 35,000 feet, then a simple tear or puncture could be disastrous. The air within the airplane explodes outward through the small tear—ripping the metal as it goes. The first jet airliners suffered from this problem. Two de Havilland Comets exploded in flight.

Therefore, the engineers built a fail-safe feature into the Hercules. If the skin is punctured or torn, the explosive decompression will take place. But the metal will tear for only a very short distance beyond the original puncture because the Hercules has rip-stop safety. It is constructed so that any fuselage tear can travel only a distance of inches—and there the rip comes to a stop.

Let us take another look at the cargo compartment. At the rear of the Hercules is a unique end-loading ramp. The entire rear bottom of the airplane, including the fuselage where it slants upward, is a loading ramp. The ramp can be lowered to any height desired. Heavy loads can be rolled right off trucks into the Hercules.

The Hercules also has a highly efficient mechanical cargo-loading system. On the floor of the airplane crewmen place special racks of roller bearings. Running overhead, the length of the fuselage, is a power-driven loading system. And here is how it works:

The Air Force, for example, wants heavy cargo loads flown to a remote site in South America. It needs them flown quickly, and with one airplane if possible. So the Hercules is called upon.

The airplane flies to the base where 35,000 pounds of cargo is ready and waiting. Normally it takes hours to load the many crates and boxes into an airplane. But these are already packaged onto special cargo pallets, and the pallets are loaded onto a long trailer. When the airplane lands, it taxis to the cargo-loading dock. The loadmaster aboard the Hercules lowers the ramp at the end of the airplane until it is at exactly the same height as the trailer. The trailer then backs up to the loading ramp.

Two men in the C-130B crew attach their loading cables to the first pallet. It weighs 15,000 pounds—but only these two men are going to handle the loading operation. The cable hooks are fastened to the cargo pallet; the power winch starts to pull, and in less than a minute the heavy pallet is loaded deep within the airplane. Because the rear cargo door is ten feet wide and nine feet high even the bulky pallets slide in without trouble.

The two crewmen slide the loading bar back to pick up the next two pallets, each weighing 10,000 pounds. Less than five minutes after they started loading, the job is done. They lash down the cargo with chains and cables to special tie-down points. The rear ramp comes up and locks into place, and the Hercules starts back for the runway, ready to begin its trip to South America.

In addition to the rear loading ramp, the Hercules also has a huge side door for cargo. The mission of the Hercules is one of both war and of peace, and there are times when it is necessary to get cargo and men in and out of the airplane fast. With the Hercules there is no wasted motion. In remote or jungle fields there are no elaborate facilities for loading and unloading. The ability of the airplane to handle its own cargo loads is one of the great advances in aviation.

The Hercules can easily carry out its dual cargo mission. This means to supply cargo normally—on the ground. But it also means aerial delivery. Its crews consider the Hercules the best airplane ever built for delivering men, tanks, equipment, cargo, and other loads from the air to the ground by parachute.

It is an unusually fast airplane for its size and design. However, it also has outstanding slow flight characteristics. The pilot can ease off on his power until the airplane is droning along at 100 to 140 miles per hour. He can fly at any speed he desires. The gaping cargo door means that huge loads can be dumped from the airplane in flight, and lowered safely by parachute.

The airplane has a specially designed mechanical aerial delivery system. It is so efficient, and the Her-

cules' power is so great, that the airplane holds the world's record for one air drop. The Hercules has dumped into the air a single load weighing 41,740 pounds. That is 13,000 pounds heavier than a fully-loaded C-47 transport. And Hercules drops such massive loads to earth without as much as a scratch.

Because of its unique loading features and the freight-car-sized cargo compartment, the Hercules can rapidly load trucks, tractors, graders, loaded trailers, and machinery such as huge electrical generators and dynamos. It can carry tanks, armored vehicles, and other heavy military weapons.

Normally the C-130B Hercules flies with a maximum payload of 37,300 pounds. But without giving up any of its safety features, the airplane can carry as much as 55,000 pounds of cargo. It is possible to roll a bulldozer and a truck into the Hercules, and still have room for a dozen men plus other equipment.

But what makes all this pay off is the Hercules' performance in the field. Almost every big airplane needs long, hard, expensive runways. In fact, its usefulness is determined by whether or not giant runways are available for it to land.

Holding perfect drop formation, waves of Hercules air-assault transports release heavy cargo loads (top). As the parachutes open, a second wave of Hercules drops its cargo which is drawn from the planes by small drogue parachutes. (*U.S. Air Force*)

An emergency mission in South America—an RC-130A Hercules lands on a dirt strip at Rio Haucha, Colombia. The Hercules flew in a helicopter, medical team, and supplies to help fight an epidemic. (*U.S. Air Force*)

The Hercules is the first of the very big transport airplanes that has complete freedom from concrete. It does not need a hard runway. It does not need a long runway. It can land and take off from runways made of dirt; grass fields will do, and so will a country road, or even a sandy field.

In terms of special cargo such as machinery, this gives the users of the Hercules unique freedom. It means that the Hercules can drop into almost any clear area 2,000 feet long, or less. The bulldozers and trucks roll out of the airplane, and are right at the spot where they are needed.

Perhaps there isn't *any* field where the airplane can land. So a few Hercules fly over the area picked for development. Bulldozers, tractors, road graders and other machinery spill into the air. Parachutes open and lower the machinery to earth. Engineers parachute down minutes later. In a few hours the bulldozers have gouged out a level area; the graders have pounded it down. It may still be rough and bumpy, but that does not matter to the Hercules. It can land almost anywhere —and now it lands on a rough strip built by the equipment it delivered only hours before.

The preunitized freight system, with its pallets, is considered a revolution in cargo. On these pallets, a huge load weighing 35,000 pounds or more can be unloaded from the Hercules, and another cargo loaded aboard, in less than 15 minutes. To do the same job with other big airplanes takes three to four hours.

The Hercules is also a modern Noah's ark on wings. Dozens of these airplanes have carried all sorts of livestock—horses, cows, pigs, sheep, fish (in special tanks), and other animals. In the pressurized, air-conditioned

A giant C-130B with gear and flaps down rumbles from the sky. Any open space can serve as a landing field for the rugged Hercules. (*Lockheed-Georgia*)

fuselage they have carried them from continent to continent in safety and comfort.

The Hercules has served as an aerial pipeline, delivering fuel and water to military and civilian construction projects in remote areas. Using rough dirt or grass strips, the airplane airlifts drums, metal or rubber tanks, or even entire tank trucks. The Hercules carries water in the fuselage, and uses its own "wet wing" for fuel. At a site in the field, engineers can drain 40,000 pounds of excess fuel from the Hercules wing tanks.

The freight-car-sized cargo compartment enables the Hercules to haul massive special purpose vans wherever needed. Let us say there has been a major disaster, such as an earthquake or a flood. Hundreds and perhaps thousands of people are in need of medical aid. Any airplane can carry medical supplies, but the Hercules can carry them in great quantities, and land almost anywhere for on-the-site delivery. Even more important, great vans can be rolled into the Hercules, flown to the disaster area, and unloaded at the spot. With power equipment, the vans are lighted and air-conditioned, and can operate as emergency medical-aid stations and hospitals. This means mobile operating rooms, sanitation units, powerful electrical supply generators, machine shops, communications centers, and even prefab shelters can be delivered where they are desperately needed.

Just as important, the Hercules can evacuate refugees from the disaster areas in great numbers. But what if these people are sick or injured? After unloading the cargo, the Hercules' crewmen move rapidly through the airplane. Special supports and stanchions unfold and snap into place. Less than sixty minutes after the vans roll out of the airplane, men are carrying stretcher patients aboard. Seventy-four litter cases, plus doctors and attendants, can be flown at nearly 360 miles per hour to the nearest hospitals.

These are some of the things that the Hercules does. Now let us see how it does them.

TO DO THE JOB 3

EVERY PILOT reacts with caution to a new airplane. No matter what he has heard from other pilots, he must decide for himself. And the only way he can do this is to get his hands around the control yoke and "let her loose."

Almost all pilots react the same way to the Hercules assault transport. Even before they can secure their seat belts and shoulder harnesses, the first impression has been made. And it can't help being an extremely good one.

Pilots for years have carried on a running feud with aircraft engineers. Most engineers design a cockpit or a flight deck to certain minimum requirements. They want to use as little space as possible, because the greater the room for the crew the less room there is available for cargo and passengers. This means that instruments, controls, seats, and everything else are invariably jammed into a small space, and this leaves much to be desired.

When the Lockheed engineers began to create the

Hercules, they spent weeks and months with pilots. They flew with transport pilots under all conditions. They flew by day and by night, over mountains and across oceans, in good weather and in raging storms. They watched the crews, listened to their complaints, and took notes.

The "front office" of the Hercules is what pilots have wanted for many years. It is a panoramic flight station with more than forty square feet of wide-angle window space. This is important to crews who must fly tight formation by day and night. Their navigation must be perfect in order to drop paratroopers and heavy loads. When it comes to those deliberate crash landings . . . well, you can't beat seeing what's coming at you.

The special Nesa glass windshields are complete sys-

The Hercules flight deck has more than 40 square feet of special glass. (*U.S. Air Force*)

tems that provide maximum visibility under all conditions—ice, fog, heat, and whatever else may be encountered. It is easy to realize how vital this is to pilots who operate one week in the Sahara Desert with the temperature at 140 degrees or hotter; the week following they may be in the Arctic or even the Antarctic, where temperatures at ground level plummet to 60 to 90 degrees below zero.

It may seem strange to describe a military assault transport as having "spaciousness, comfort, and convenience" for the crew. After all, they aren't exactly out for maximum luxury. But that is not the case at all. Hercules missions may keep a crew on the go for weeks. After flying a certain number of hours, any human being loses efficiency. Pilots are under a great strain, especially when flying through strange and even dangerous parts of the world. In a high-performance airplane like the Hercules, there is not much room for mistakes. So comfort and convenience are built into the airplane to get the greatest possible service from the crew, and to keep the airplane in operation on a day-to-night basis. The seats are scientifically designed so that a man can sit in them for as long as fourteen hours and still be able to perform with razor-like precision when necessary.

In the Hercules flight deck the galley is even equipped with an oven for preparing meals. There are hot food containers, a refrigerator, and a sink. The bunks (double-deck) are comfortable. If a crew is on a mission where they must keep on the move for several days, they team up with a second crew. While one group of men flies, the second group catches up on its sleep. They shift, back and forth.

Airplanes were flown under emergency conditions for years before the Hercules. And the crews, when they worked as one-team-on and one-team-off, didn't like it one bit. They did their work, but they were extremely uncomfortable. Crew efficiency suffered when a pilot who was on the go for weeks couldn't get a decent rest.

As the Hercules piled up years of experience, pilots began to compare notes. Many men who hadn't flown in the Hercules simply didn't believe the things they heard about crew conveniences and scientific design. And when they did find out that it was all true, there was a near stampede by dozens of crews to become assigned to a real "pilot's airplane."

And there is the key to its enduring success—it is a pilot's airplane. But there are reasons for this other than comfort. To earn the accolade of pilot's airplane, a ship must deliver in all respects. Comfort isn't enough. There is no use being comfortable if the airplane is difficult to fly, or if it breaks down repeatedly.

To become a pilot's airplane, the machine must perform right down the line. It must present a minimum of headaches for all crew members. It must be reliable mechanically. It can't have any faults that spring without warning at a pilot, such as dipping a wing at low speed near the ground. In other words, the airplane must be versatile and reliable, no matter what demands are placed upon it.

For example, the position of an instrument, or a group of instruments, before the pilot can cause an accident. The manner in which instruments can be read, the way they are illuminated at night, are all extremely important to good performance. When a pilot is in trouble, in a violent storm or in battle, he hasn't time to look around to get information. It must be instantly available to him. The controls must be free of obstructions, instantly recognizable. They must be scientifically located in the flight deck. Even their size, length, and shape must be carefully determined.

Lockheed engineers did the same kind of patient research for instruments and controls as they did with the rest of the flight deck. They shaped every control handle, where possible, to anthropometric measurements, that is to those most easily grasped by the hand or fingers. When they built the electrical and the fuel-system controls and instruments, they combined them with schematic diagrams to simplify their operation.

Hauling an airplane weighing sixty to seventy tons through the air is not an easy task. When a pilot is cruising in level flight at high altitude, an automatic pilot can do much of his work for him. And in the Hercules, as in every other new transport, there is an elaborate autopilot system.

But what happens when the pilot must fly through storms? How about holding tight formation with other

The powerful Hercules can fly tight formation with fingertip control. The four transports are flying with an aerobatic team known as the Four Horsemen. (*U.S. Air Force*)

airplanes, especially when the air is turbulent, and the propellers of the other airplanes hurl back rivers of swirling air? There is the problem of maneuvering at slow flight, of crash-landing deliberately into small fields. There is the need to twist and turn in mountainous terrain. All of these tasks, and many others, can quickly drain the strength of any pilot. They can slow down his reflexes at the controls because of the sheer muscle power needed to push the big machine around.

To eliminate this problem, Lockheed built the Hercules with hydraulic muscle in the controls. The pilot has the strength of a dozen men helping him to maneuver the airplane. This is known as the power-boost control system.

Whenever the pilot operates his control yoke or his rudder pedals, special instruments sense the movement. To go into a right turn, the pilot must use both his ailerons and his rudder. The ailerons are hinged control surfaces at the trailing edge of the wings, near the tips. To perform the turn to the right, the pilot turns the control yoke to the right and presses down on the right rudder pedal. It is a smooth, coordinated movement of both controls.

Normally, an airplane has a system of cables running from the pilot controls to the control surfaces in the wings and at the tail. He must exert enough physical pressure on his controls in the cockpit to move the controls in the wings and the tail against great wind forces.

Maneuvering the Hercules is finger-tip flying. As soon as the pilot moves his controls, the special instruments note the movement. Each control movement by the pilot is actually a command to a robot system, which uses hydraulic pressure to move the control cables and, also, the control surfaces.

When we press down on the accelerator of an automobile, the vehicle picks up speed. Pressing down on the accelerator can't make the car go faster, of course. But it does increase the flow of fuel to the engine. The engine operates with greater power, and transmits that power through the drive shaft to the wheels. The wheels turn faster and the car goes faster.

The control system of the Hercules is more complicated than this, but the principle is the same.

This is another and important reason why the Hercules has become known as a pilot's airplane. It can be flown with gentle pressures and instant response, no matter what the situation. The control pressures are so light that the Hercules flies like a jet fighter. Pilots new to the airplane are astonished at the "baby-carriage effort" needed to fly the Hercules. It takes awhile to become accustomed to the change. Where pilots once wrestled and fought their airplanes, they can fly the Hercules.

The first time I took the controls of the Hercules, I was in for the same surprise that met so many other pilots. We were cruising at 14,000 feet over France. The pilot was Captain Jim Ford, of the 314th Troop Carrier Wing. I sat in the copilot seat. Captain Ford told me to make a "fairly steep turn to the left; bring her around smart."

The last big airplane I'd flown, about a year before, was the Boeing B-17 Flying Fortress. The B-17 was a wonderful airplane to fly, but when you wanted full maneuvers, you had to work. Expecting the same re-action, I brought the control yoke well over to the left and pressed down with plenty of strength on the rudder.

Before I knew what was happening, the giant Hercules was rolling over into a steeper and steeper bank. The wings rolled around until they were nearly vertical! Captain Ford laughed and rolled the airplane back again to level flight. He explained that the same thing happened almost every time a pilot new to the Hercules took the controls for the first time.

REDUNDANCY MEANS RELIABILITY

Engineers are cautious people. They spend months and even years designing and creating a new airplane. There are hundreds of thousands of parts that must be integrated into the final product—parts that must blend together, and then be fitted into the machine that will fly.

But airplanes do not fly without power systems. There must be power for flight in the form of engines. And power systems to operate the radar, controls, electronic gear, landing gear, flaps, doors, lights, and a hundred other things that are just as vital.

The power systems of airplanes have been one of the great headaches of aviation engineering. They are so complicated that two things often happen. First, they break down. This means a useless airplane in need of repairs. It also means missions that must be cancelled, and emergencies in flight.

An airplane on the ground is a worthless piece of junk. Airplanes are designed to fly. They are intended to carry cargo, passengers, mail, or anything else that makes up a payload. The load must be moved to where it is needed. Because the airplane can do this faster than any other means of transportation is the reason why we have transport planes.

So when an airplane breaks down and needs expensive, time-consuming repairs, it is not worth a thing to anyone.

There is a giant transport plane that has been used for several years by the Air Force. It is considerably bigger than the Hercules. It can carry a greater load than the Hercules. Its engines are more powerful. It was designed to be a great workhorse of the skies.

Unfortunately, this giant suffers from aches and pains throughout its many complicated power systems. The aches and pains are mechanical, hydraulic, and electrical, but they have been almost disastrous to the career of the airplane. It spends much of its time on the ground. Mechanics and technicians labor day and night to keep it repaired, to get it back into the air. It is expensive to maintain; it wastes the labor of skilled men. And when it is in the hangar, its cargo can't move.

It is a colossal airplane, and one of the most colossal headaches the Air Force has ever had. Despite its great cargo capacity, few pilots, crewmen, or mechanics want anything to do with the airplane. Who wants to spend most of his time waiting for more and more repair work?

No airplane can hope to be successful unless it is outstanding in reliability. This is one of the things that made the Gooney Bird so beloved to its pilots. Even when things clanked and banged instead of running smoothly, the old Gooney kept right on plugging along.

An airplane like the Hercules, with its great size, power, and many internal systems, can easily become a nightmare of complexity. With so many systems aboard the airplane, it is easy to have things break down. It is a thousand times more difficult to build reliability into an airplane like the Hercules than it was with the Gooney Bird.

When Lockheed won the fierce competition to build the Hercules in mass production, its engineers were painfully aware of the reliability problem. They couldn't escape it. The Air Force told Lockheed they wanted an airplane that was to be:

> An advanced, all-purpose, work-horse type, aerial vehicle, that can go any place, any time, and without elaborate facility or equipment preparations.

Every engineer must consider the greatest problem in designing an airplane. No matter how excellent are the facilities for maintaining the airplane at the factory, those facilities vanish once the airplane leaves the plant. At the factory the airplane may be attended with lavish care. When it goes out into its operational life, it will have to be able to fly in every environment. This is especially true of an assault transport like the Hercules.

From the beginning there was no doubt that pilots were going to abuse the Hercules. Their missions would leave them no choice. They would have to slam the airplane down onto rough fields; they would fly through heat and cold, rain and snow, sand and ice. They would have to fly day and night in grueling endurance missions. Proper maintenance would not be available.

It would be impossible to care properly for the many systems and subsystems of the Hercules. Yet, if only one system broke down, the airplane would be crippled and grounded. Therefore, a way had to be found that would permit the Hercules to continue operating even if a critical system were to fail.

The answer lay in the concept of *redundancy*, that is, building all the critical systems of the airplane on a basis of repetition and providing a backup system wherever it might be needed. If the primary system failed, why, the airplane would still operate because of the secondary system. The mission would continue to be flown, and repairs made as quickly as circumstances allowed. But the important thing was that failure would not cripple or ground the Hercules.

The hydraulic system of the Hercules is an excellent example. Hydraulic pressure (power) is needed to operate the power-boosted controls, the massive landing gear, the loading ramp at the rear of the airplane, and other assemblies. If the hydraulic pressure failed, the Hercules could easily be crippled.

It could be, but it isn't. Within the Hercules there are four hydraulic pumps. Each is driven by the powerful jet engines of the airplane. The pumps, in turn, supply pressure for the utility systems of the Hercules, as well as the booster systems. These comprise the basic operating assemblies of the airplane. But how about the backup, in case the main hydraulic pressure fails?

Whenever the Hercules is in operation, a small but powerful electric motor runs a hydraulic pump. This pump is the source of pressure for the auxiliary, or backup, system of the airplane. During operations, either one of the hydraulic systems may fail. The pumps driven by the jet engines might suddenly lose pressure. Or the pump driven by the electric motor could suffer a breakdown.

The Hercules would keep right on operating because it has two sources of hydraulic pressure. Both sources are always in operation, and either one of them can meet the needs of the airplane.

It is as though an automobile had two engines. If anything happened to one of the two engines, or to any of its parts, the car wouldn't break down. The second engine that operates all the time would simply keep the car rolling.

The backup systems principle was a marvelous innovation for the Hercules, but it couldn't solve all problems. Any complicated system needs some maintenance in the field. Once again the engineers dreamed up the worst possible conditions. They imagined parts breaking down, or simply wearing out. And they imagined this happening in remote and isolated areas. There would be no supply warehouse, no spare parts building.

The flight engineer of the Hercules would have to make repairs, or maintain his systems, as easily as possible. Normally, repairs in the field mean tearing open panels, removing plates, and working under difficult conditions. Even testing out a system was time-consuming and difficult.

The Hercules does away with all this back-breaking effort. Instead of having hydraulic reservoirs, accumulators, valves, and other parts scattered around the airplane, they are grouped together in a single place. The central location of the complicated system is like a miracle to the flight engineer and the mechanic. Everything is built with the greatest possible simplicity. And everything is built so that it can be reached without any spinal contortions.

A mechanic can stand on the ground to check out the entire Hercules' hydraulic system. He doesn't need any ladders, high rigs, or anything else. He can remove quick-disconnect covers, and everything is right there at his fingertips. In only minutes he can study all the connections to test, check out, and care for the hydraulic system.

Hydraulic pressure meets only some of the needs of an airplane like the Hercules. It is so complex, and its missions so demanding, that it needs great electrical power as well.

The problems of hydraulic systems are bad enough, but those of electrical systems are even worse. There never seems to be enough power for all the jobs that must be done. And this means power in different forms.

Once again, the Hercules was designed with trouble in mind. The Hercules is literally a flying powerhouse. It is filled with powerful generators. They are run by different systems, with full redundancy. One system may fail entirely, but the airplane does not lose its vital electrical power. It has special transformer-rectifiers. These take electrical energy and convert it to the demands of different types of equipment. Because such a system must be complex, the crew is given as much help as possible in its operation. Elaborate but very clear schematic diagrams are integrated with the instruments and controls. They allow the crewmen to trace every part of the electrical system, and check out any assembly or unit.

One of the major problems with a large airplane is to supply it with fuel. Anyone who has spent time at our large airports learns quickly enough that this can be a cumbersome and time-consuming process. Especially if it is raining or snowing, or ice builds up on slick wings, or there are high winds. Mechanics must clamber up ladders and along the wings, balanced precariously. They drag heavy hoses with them. They must bend down to free a locking receptacle, insert the hose nozzle into the tank opening. There are several tanks to be dealt with along the wings.

Obviously, this kind of inefficiency and clumsiness could not be allowed with the Hercules. The engineers designed the C-130 to be refueled in the simplest operation possible. One man, standing on the ground, can refuel the Hercules. He has a single-point receptacle into which he places the fuel hose. In front of him is a control panel, located in the fairing for the main right landing gear. The mechanic works the controls of the panel, and the fuel flows from this one point into the tanks.

There are four large fuel tanks integral with the Hercules' wing which is known as a wet wing. Certain models, like the C-130A and the C-130E, have large tanks suspended beneath the wings. All of them can be refueled through this one receptacle.

But suppose the Hercules is operating at a remote field? Normal fueling facilities may not be available. This, too, was considered. Atop the wings are additional fuel tank filler caps to meet any situation including fueling the airplane by hand from kerosene cans.

The unique fueling system of the Hercules allows it to function as a rescue airplane. Suppose a Hercules or any other modern airplane is on the ground in a remote site, without any fuel. Flying in fuel can be a difficult job, especially when the fuel must be transferred from drums to an airplane. The Hercules ended those problems quickly.

The versatility of Hercules as a flying gas station is shown as Royal Canadian Air Force crews deliver fuel oil to Arctic stations. (*Lockheed-Georgia*)

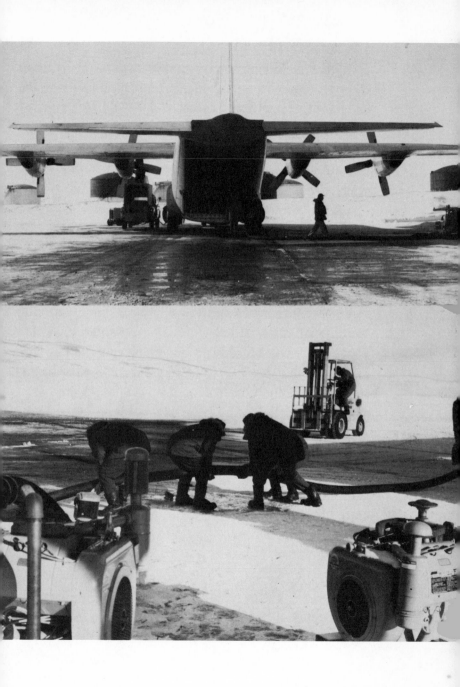

A special fueling system makes it possible to drain through hoses, quickly, many tons of fuel from the wing tanks. That fuel is then transferred to the other airplane, and both transports fly out.

Then the Air Force came up with their own innovation in emergency fueling. They built huge tanks which could be rolled into the cargo hold of the Hercules. Along with the tanks went hoses, controls, and pumps. Then they filled the interior tanks with nearly 40,000 pounds of jet fuel.

In the first test of the flying gasoline station, six powerful jet fighters roared into a remote airport almost out of fuel. Soon afterward a Hercules thundered onto the airstrip, and pulled close to the fighters. The big cargo ramp clanged down, men came running out with hoses. Within seconds the hoses were linked to the fighters, and fuel was flowing into their tanks.

The test deliberately created problems. With all the fuselage fuel drained, one fighter still was short on kerosene. The Hercules crew drained fuel from their own wing tanks and transferred that fuel to the remaining fighter. Minutes later the six jets screamed into the air to complete their mission, the Hercules close behind.

TANKERS IN THE SKY

The original mission of the Hercules was to haul cargo. But the first airplane hadn't even taken to the air when that mission began to grow. More and more jobs were piled on the Hercules. The Air Force ordered many different versions, and so did the Navy, the Coast Guard, and the Marines.

Early in 1962, the Marines were fully operational with their shining new KC-130F Hercules. These were multimission airplanes. They met all Marine Corps requirements for a troop transport and paradrop airplane. They were to be used for cargo and rescue missions. And they were also the first flying tankers the Marines had ever had.

Before the Hercules, when the Marines sent fighter units to overseas bases, it had usually been a slow and tedious job. The fighters went by surface—by slow, crawling ship. Once in a while Marine fighters were able to refuel from Air Force tankers. But not very often, and the Marines were restricted to the range of their jets.

And then came the KC-130F tankers, and the Marine Corps shifted to overseas movements "by air all the way."

On the first mission, Operation Pine Needles, eighteen big F8U Crusader jet fighters left California to fly across the Pacific in a record flight, for the Marines, of 7,100 miles. Thirteen Hercules tankers moved into position along the route, cruising over the vast expanse of the Pacific. They made 108 hookups with the Marine fighters—108 actual connections by fueling hoses to the fighters. And each time fuel poured from the

A KC-130F Hercules holds steady in formation flight as two A4D attack jets ride in close for refueling. Notice the long hose probes extending back from each wing of the Marine tanker-transport. (*U.S. Navy*)

Hercules tankers into the Crusaders. The mission was a brilliant success.

Several weeks later the Hercules were back along the same route. This time they poured fuel into eighteen delta-winged Skyhawk jet attack bombers. Once again the mission went perfectly.

And then came the night of April 2, 1962—at

Iwakuni airbase in Japan an airplane crashed as it landed on the runway. The weather was "murder," one pilot said. Fog hung low over the ground, and closed the field.

Above the clouds were four of the big Crusader fighters. As they penetrated the mists, radar controllers guided them accurately to the runway. But because of the crash they could not land. Hastily the Crusaders boomed upward through the clouds again.

The Marine pilots were in serious trouble. They couldn't land at Iwakuni yet they lacked the fuel to fly to the nearest open field—Atsugi. The pilots faced a grim choice. They would head their heavy jets out to sea. Then, at night and in a storm, they would eject. If the ejection seats, the parachutes, and the life rafts all worked—and they were found in time—they could survive.

But four Marine Hercules were in the air. Their pilots received a frantic radio call for assistance. The four tankers wheeled sharply and rushed at top speed for a rendezvous with the Crusaders. But the big airplanes were not carrying their tanker fuel loads.

Now an old premise paid off. The engineers who had designed the Hercules had been told: "Always assume the airplane will be in the worst possible position. Give it the greatest versatility possible, to meet the unexpected."

In the tankers, Marine crewmen twisted valves and worked fuel-control switches. From the bulbous housings beneath the wings long hoses snaked back. At the end of each hose was a wide drogue. The fighter pilot had to ram a probe on his airplane into the drogue, and hold it there, in order to refuel.

But what about that lack of fuel aboard the Hercules? The tanker system, which is exclusive with the Hercules, enables the crew to feed fuel to fighters right from the Hercules' own wing tanks. The Hercules was feeding its own fuel to the fighters.

That is why the tanker pilots called out to the fighters to "come on in and fill 'em up." The four Crusaders gulped the fuel, and broke free. They set their course for a distant field where all the planes landed safely.

The four Hercules transports failed to complete their cargo mission that night. But no one really cared about that!

THE BIG PUSH 4

WHEN THE Hercules comes to life, it commands attention. People standing anywhere close to the airplane listen to everything that takes place. They haven't any choice, the noise is often a thunderous din.

In the bulging left gear housing is concealed a powerful gas turbine compressor (GTC). It is one of the items built into the Hercules that adds to its reputation as both a pilot's airplane and a mechanic's dream. The GTC frees the Hercules from the bulky ground equipment many airplanes need to begin their first moments of life before a flight.

The flight engineer starts the compressor, and the sound that bursts from the GTC cracks out like a high-pitched bullwhip. The GTC builds up almost immediately to full power. The loudest engine I've ever heard is a comfortable lullaby compared to the sound of the GTC. It is a mixture of great thunder and a hoarse shriek. It stabs the ears like two sharp knives.

But it is the key to that cherished freedom from ground equipment. From the GTC, air howls within ducts to start the Allison jet engines. The GTC serves in other ways as well. On the ground it provides air conditioning (hot or cold air) for the airplane. It preheats the engine nacelles before the jets are started. And it provides the power for an air turbine motor which, in turn, drives an electrical generator.

It may be devastating to the ears, but the GTC is one of the most marvelous devices ever put into an airplane.

The newcomer to the Hercules is startled by the sound. Not only because of the hoarse shriek—but because despite all that noise nothing seems to be happening. The propellers don't move, and the airplane sits without a tremor.

In the flight deck, however, the crew is already working. The four men in the flight deck—pilot, copilot, engineer, and navigator—operate by a checklist. They don't do a thing without referring to the printed checklist. One hundred sixty-four separate steps are required to start all the systems and subsystems of the Hercules. No man can possibly remember them all.

The first indication an observer has of the Hercules coming to life is the slow turning of a propeller. There is no grinding complaint of metal, as is heard with the piston engine. There is no clattering roar and a burst of smoke as the engine catches.

The Allison jet engine turns slowly at first. Then the individual propeller blades begin to blur with movement. The sound of the engine begins low and builds up steadily, but it remains unheard because of the howl of the GTC.

Then, almost before the onlookers realize it has happened, the turning propeller is a gleaming blur of faint silver. Another propeller begins to turn, and then another. Finally all four jets are spinning under full power. The flight engineer closes down the GTC. In its last burst of noise it sounds like a wounded dinosaur rolling over to die.

Now the sound of the Hercules is heard clearly. The deep thrumming cry of this airplane is unmistakable. As the sound varies, people listening think they can hear the effect of the throttles being moved back and forth as the pilot changes power. But they are wrong. The turboprop is a contradiction of what is normal in propeller-driven airplanes.

The changing sound takes place when the pilot changes the angle—the pitch—at which the propeller blades bite into the air. It is the propellers that create most of the noise from an airplane, not the engine. With the Hercules the sound is particularly distinctive. There is no thrashing of pistons or clattering of parts, as with the piston engine. There is no continuous process of explosions in cylinder walls.

The jet engines whirl at nearly 14,000 revolutions per minute. Their power is reduced through a gearing system so that the propellers whirl at about 1,020 revolutions per minute (rpm).

Those Wonderful Allisons

The first YC-130 Hercules took to the skies in the summer of 1954. It seems difficult to believe that this giant is already ten years old, because there still isn't any competition in sight for this airplane's sensational performance.

We have seen many of the features that make the Hercules a pilot's airplane. But none is more important than its source of power for flight—the four Allison jet engines, geared to the wide-bladed propellers. Pilots call them "instant power."

In 1956, when the Hercules was still considered an experimental airplane, Air Force pilots studied the machine cautiously. The turboprop concept was new. The latest transport airplanes were featuring low, swept-back wings. Pure jet power was the answer, most people felt. Then what about this squat and massive new machine? How would it do?

Major Joseph P. Tracy of the Air Force's Flight Safety Division was one of the first pilots to get his hands on the Hercules. And what he said made Air Force pilots everywhere take extra notice of the transport.

> "It is not particularly a big airplane when compared with such aircraft as the C-124 or the C-133," wrote Major Tracy, "but it appears now that it can carry a whopping load . . . and beat the

tar out of its bigger brothers when it comes to speed.

"The C-130 is one of the first turboprop jobs and from the limited flight experience with the plane . . . such type power is here to stay. You'll be seeing more and more of these high-tailed dudes in the near future. The front of the C-130 resembles a goat but you may rest assured that its nowhere near as stubborn.

"You run the power levers up to maximum . . . release the brakes and rather casually nudge the nosewheel steering as needed, and in nothing flat you're airborne. Eight hundred feet or so ground run and—jump!"

When the Hercules first took to the air for its exhaustive test program, no one knew quite how the engines would work out. In theory they were fine. How would they perform when pilots abused the airplanes, flew in all kinds of weather, and ran the engines far beyond "safe" operation?

The Hercules test program created many more problems than is normal for such work. The airplane was completely new. The wing was a new design. The structure represented many innovations. And the engines—well, pilots didn't accept those at all.

Jack G. Gilley, the Aviation Safety Staff Engineer of Lockheed-Georgia, recalls the test program:

"Both the airplane and the engines achieved their

success together. All the odds were against this. I think that all of us who were on the flight test program were convinced that we had picked a winner. You have a feeling about this sort of thing, and it turned out that we were right."

Test Pilot Vern Peterson explains that the power of the engines "is what makes the Hercules so incredibly safe. You always have the power to get out of a jam if things start coming unglued."

Walt Hensleigh as a test pilot flew the Hercules more than a thousand hours in its development program:

"I've flown multiengine airplanes for most of my career," he explains. "On the basis of my experience with many airplane types, the C-130 has been just about the most *un*exciting airplane I ever flew. It just hasn't put us up against the wall like many other ships are inclined to do. Oh sure, we've lost engines in flight and run into other mechanical difficulties that with other airplanes meant hitting the panic button.

"But the Hercules is so terrific in its power . . . that the emergencies never amount to very much. . . . We can carry just about anything you can cram into the airplane, and if necessary we can carry it just as well with only three engines operating. And once we really get up steam, we can do it on two engines."

Let us look at some of the situations that arose once Hercules went into operation. It is one thing for test pilots and engineers to be enthusiastic about their airplane. They live with it for months and years, and they come to know its every habit. But what about men who are new to the airplane?

The Coast Guard uses the Hercules for many missions, among them search-and-rescue. When an airliner over the ocean loses an engine, for example, a Hercules races out to meet the airplane. It escorts it to the nearest airport. As it flies with the crippled airliner, it sends out strong radio signals to confirm the position of the airplanes at all times. If the airliner must ditch, that is land in the water, the Hercules broadcasts distress calls for help. It also drops liferafts and emergency equipment to the downed crew and passengers.

On one occasion a big DC-7C airliner ran into serious trouble approaching the United States. The DC-7C lost all power in one engine, and the crew had to shut down the engine and feather the propeller. The DC-7C can fly on three engines, but to do that it must drop down to 10,000 feet. With a full passenger complement of men, women, and many children, the pilot broadcasted his distress call.

A Coast Guard Hercules thundered out of San Francisco. The two airplanes met over the Pacific. The Hercules came swinging around in a wide turn until it was flying alongside the crippled airliner.

The crew and passengers of the DC-7C gaped as they looked at the Hercules, for the Coast Guard pilot had shut down his two outboard engines. The big propellers stabbed lifelessly into the wind. As the airliner pilot stared, the Coast Guard pilot grinned at him.

Long-range missions with only two engines operating are standard for the Hercules.

To prove this point in a dramatic fashion, an Air Force crew took off one morning from a Florida airbase. Instead of climbing to high altitude where the Hercules cruises efficiently, the pilot kept the airplane down low. And I mean low—he skimmed trees and hilltops.

Then he turned to his engineer and said: "Okay— shut 'em down." The engineer nodded, and casually shut down the number one and four engines.

Flying on only two engines, loaded with fuel, the Hercules raced toward California. It stayed low all the way across the United States, hedgehopping and skipping over mountains. A pilot recalls what happened:

"It was some trip. They beat up the countryside all the way from Florida to California.

"They've still got warrants out for those guys in quite a few cities, because in every town and village and city they passed over, or nearby, people sort of got excited. They saw this big airplane, something entirely new to them, and with a sound they'd never heard before.

"Big airplanes don't fly low—and this one was right *on* the deck. And big airplanes don't normally fly with two of the engines dead and the props feathered. The airplane burst into view without warning, howled overhead, and just disappeared from sight over the nearest hill.

"Well, what else could this mean except that this monster was on its way down to a crash? Everyone figured that it had gone out of sight and then smashed into a hill or plowed into a mountain. People by the hundreds called the police to report the disaster. Everybody wanted to know—'where did it crash?' "

One pilot had occasion to appreciate the power of the Allison jet engine—*not* engines—of his Hercules. Lieutenant Jocko Donlon of the 839th Air Division was flying a heavily loaded Hercules when he was caught

"It was some trip. They beat up the countryside all the way from Florida to California. And on *two* engines!" is the way one observer described a rough Hercules flight. (*U.S. Air Force*)

in a violent thunderstorm. Without warning the airplane was bombarded with giant hailstones the size of golf balls.

This is one of the most terrifying experiences in aviation. Imagine the sound of an airplane being smashed with thousands of golf balls hitting the airplane at more than three hundred miles per hour.

The barrage of hail smashed and pounded the oil cooler ducts of the engines. It twisted and bent them so badly that it choked off the flow of cooling air to the engines. Without that cooling air, the temperatures skyrocketed in the engines. The fire warning lights on the panel blinked brilliant red, and Lieutenant Donlon had no choice but to shut down the engines and feather the propellers.

That left him with one engine and a heavily loaded airplane.

The engineer squeezed every ounce of power he could from the engine. The airplane was so heavily loaded that there didn't seem to be enough time to get the ramp down, the cargo unlashed, and then to dump the cargo. Lieutenant Donlon eased the nose down to help the laboring airplane, and on a long slant he headed for the nearest airport.

It seemed absolutely impossible, but he made it.

INSTANT POWER

Just as important as the power of the Allison engine is its ability to absorb tremendous punishment and abuse.

One Hercules on a search mission over the Pacific flew for hours through torrential downpours with the two outboard engines shut down. The men aboard could hardly believe their eyes when they looked at the engines that weren't operating. A heavy stream of water was pouring from the rear of each engine.

After several hours of this, the pilots fired up the two engines. The Allisons started immediately, and in seconds were whirling at full power.

Another pilot told me about special Air Force tests on rough fields in the early days of the Hercules.

"We'd come down with a real crash stop," he said. "We'd just slam the airplane down on the field, and then it would disappear completely from sight in all the dust that blew up. It just disappears. You can't see a thing for all that dust. It fascinates me to think that those engines can eat that much dust and keep right on going as though they were cruising at twenty thousand feet in perfectly clear and clean air . . ."

Another feature about which everybody is enthusiastic is the simplicity of the Allison engine. It has proved to be one of the most reliable engines ever built. This is extremely important. Engine difficulties have plagued many big airplanes. Time spent on the ground for maintenance cripples flight schedules. Changing an engine is a time-consuming, complicated, and expensive process that takes a crew of skilled men, elaborate facilities, and hundreds of man-hours. But not with a Hercules!

In July, 1959, a regular Air Force maintenance crew rolled a C-130 into a hangar. They removed all four T56 engines. Then they installed four new engines, hooked up all the wiring and plumbing, and ran the systems through a careful check. Time required from beginning to end of the entire operation—only five hours.

THE HARDWARE

The Allison T56 engine in the C-130B airplane is only 145 inches in length and 27 inches in diameter. Even more important, the T56 engine weighs only 1,610 pounds.

No matter how you look at it, that is a small engine for an airplane as big as the Hercules. But it is small only in size and weight—it is a giant in power. Each T56 engine turns out 4,050 horsepower.

When you consider that the T56 operates while chewing sand, dust, snow, ice, water, or air, that it runs at 100 per cent power all the time, in extremes of temperature, it is all the more remarkable.

Another way to look at the Allison is by the weight-to-power ratio. Each engine produces two-and-a-quarter horsepower for each pound of engine weight. Added up, that comes to 16,200 horsepower for the airplane.

This can be compared to the 2,400 horsepower total for the DC-3. The Boeing B-17 Flying Fortress produced a total of 4,800 horsepower for all its four en-

The Allison engine, developing 4,050 horsepower, is rugged and reliable, and one of the easiest engines for mechanics to service and maintain. (*U.S. Air Force*)

gines, which is not much more than the power of one T56 engine in the Hercules.

Each T56 engine consists of two assemblies—the power section, or gas turbine, and the reduction gear assembly, which has a single propeller shaft.

The turbine is long and slender. It has an axial-flow compressor made up of fourteen compact compressors.

These take in air, ram it to high pressure (compressed air), and then whip it backward. The compressed air slams into six combustion chambers. Here it is mixed with the fuel, and the fuel-air mixture (like the spray from an aerosol bomb) is then ignited. The tremendous pressure from this burning process creates the driving power of the engine. The blazing gases howl back to a four-stage turbine. The gases strike the blades of the turbine to spin the turbine at speeds up to nearly 14,000 revolutions per minute.

The result of this process is what makes the Hercules go. The spinning turbine itself turns the propeller shaft, the shaft whirls the propeller, and the propeller provides thrust. There is even an additional gain because of the jet engine. The exhaust gases stream back from the airplane with enough force to contribute 15 per cent of the total thrust to the airplane.

An Air Force instructor once explained the T56 engine to pilots who had never flown a turboprop this way:

"It is a jet engine that utilizes more energy toward driving a prop shaft and less energy for jet propulsion.

"This gives us propeller efficiency at low altitudes where we really need it. And we get high performance upstairs at altitudes for the long flights.

"There's another factor in favor of this arrangement, and that is simplicity. There aren't any connecting rods to clank and bang. No pistons to push and pull and hammer and no rings. Combustion and electrical timing problems? In this engine there aren't any. Fuel problems? None. As a matter of fact, the T56 engine will digest almost anything. Of course, the regular JP-4 kerosene fuel is what we'd like to have everybody use in the airplane. But in a pinch, when nothing else is available, the T56 will operate on almost anything that will flow, and that can burn."

A BIGGER BITE OF AIR

The throttles on the Hercules work like those of any airplane. The pilot advances (pushes) the throttles to gain more power, and he retards (pulls back) on the throttles to reduce power. The airplane reacts as does other airplanes. But there is a big difference in what happens with the engines and propellers of the Hercules. That system does *not* work the same way and it is the key to the performance of the Hercules.

Let us look at the system in the piston-engine airplane first. When the pilot wants to add speed, he does two things.

First, he moves his propeller control to the forward position. This changes the pitch of the propeller blades and the angle at which they bite into the air. The pilot flattens out the pitch—moves it into "fine" position. The blades shift position as they turn. Now their sharp edges are cutting almost knifelike into the air.

As the propeller spins, there is less drag on the blades—less air resistance to their spinning. Because of the lowered resistance, the workload on the engine is reduced. The engine automatically speeds up its operation.

Then the pilot advances his throttle to maximum power. Now the flow of fuel into the engine increases. Higher temperatures result from this increased burning of fuel. The heat from this process drives the propeller shaft, and increases further the speed at which the propeller turns.

A propeller blade is actually a small wing. When it turns in the air, the air flows over and beneath the blades, exactly as it does with the fixed wing on the airplane. The movement of air is carefully shaped by the curving blade. This movement results in less pressure in the front of the propeller blade than there is directly behind the blade.

A high-pressure area will always try to push its way into an area of lower pressure. Since the air pressure behind the blade is greater than in front, the air tries to move from the back to the front of the blade. But the blade is in the way, and the movement of air is applied against the blade itself. This is a physical force. With several blades to each propeller, the forward force, or thrust, is multiplied. With the propellers turning at great speed, it is multiplied even more. And this is how an airplane derives its forward thrust, or push, from its propellers.

The purpose of every propeller is to move a mass of air from the front of the propeller to the rear. The greater the mass of air that is moved, the greater the differences in pressure.

Thus the greatest power is derived from the movement of the greatest mass of air.

When a propeller is in "coarse pitch," the blades are slicing through the air at an angle. There is more resistance to their movement. You can demonstrate this yourself when swimming. Move your hand through the water knife-edge—with the side of your hand moving first. There is not much resistance. Then move your hand through the water with your palm facing in the direction of the movement. There is more drag, or resistance, to the movement of your hand. It takes more muscle power to move your hand. In fact, you can't move your hand through the water in this fashion as fast as you can when the side of your palm is pushed through the water.

A propeller and its blades work the same way. More drag means that a greater mass of air is being moved. But the piston-engine airplane can not deliver full power with the propeller in coarse pitch. The load on the engine is so great from air drag that the turning speed of the engine drops and so does the speed of the propeller.

The piston engine-propeller system is a compromise. It gets its greatest forward thrust when the propeller spins the fastest and with the least drag from the movement of the propeller.

Now, the Hercules system is exactly the opposite. Instead of trying to get rid of propeller drag, it uses that drag to get more power. It can do this because the Allison jet engines are so powerful themselves. They allow the propellers to take a bigger bite of air without slowing down.

The key to understanding the power the Hercules gets through its propellers lies in the gear-reduction system of the engines.

The C-130A model has engines that spin at the tremendous speed of 13,820 revolutions per minute. That means the engine is whirling around more than 230 times every second.

The propeller also turns at a constant speed, but more slowly than the engine. The propeller turns at 1,016 revolutions per minute. The ratio of engine speed to propeller speed is 13.6, that is, the engine spins 13.6 times faster than the propeller.

A pilot would never change the turning speed of his propellers. But he could shift the pitch of the blades from fine to coarse without losing any of that turning speed. This instantly increases the mass of air being moved. It also means more thrust and instant power with instant performance.

Here is how it works:

The pilot is cruising at 200 miles per hour. He wants maximum power from his engines to build up speed quickly to 360 miles per hour. So he moves the power levers (throttles) full forward. Now begins the automatic sequence of events.

Remember, however, that "sequence" is not really the correct word. The whole process takes place at almost the same time. But for our purposes of explanation, we'll stretch them out a bit.

When the throttles move forward, the propellers shift pitch. They take a bigger bite of the air, and try to move a greater mass of air to the rear of the propellers.

Shifting to coarse pitch increases the drag on the propellers. And this is where the reduction-gear system comes in. The engine is turning nearly fourteen times faster than the propeller. When the blades shift position and increase drag, they increase the workload of the engine as well.

Automatically, the system shifts its gears. The propellers are allowed to squeeze power from the engines. Despite the tremendous drag of the turning propellers, they don't slow down one bit. The mass of air moving past the propellers is much greater, and the airplane leaps ahead.

But even in an airplane you never get something for nothing. Where does all that power come from? We know that the engine is turning at 13,820 rpm. But if the gear system transfers its energy from the engine to the propellers, how can the engine keep on delivering all that energy?

The answer lies in the fuel-feed system. Remember, we said there was the equivalent of a robot brain controlling the whole process.

Here—step-by-step—is what happens:

1) The pilot wants more speed so he advances the throttles.

2) The propellers automatically shift into coarse pitch. They move a greater air mass to the rear of the airplane. This increases the forward thrust, and the airplane increases its speed.

3) The robot brain senses the increased drag on the propellers. Immediately it shifts the gears of the engine-propeller systems. It squeezes the engines of power, and transfers this power to the propellers. With more power, the propellers overcome the increased resistance of air drag, and the speed continues to increase.

4) The engines have given up energy, and it must be replaced. The robot brain goes into action again. The power of the engines comes from heat. The engines burn fuel and oxygen. This process of combustion yields great heat or yields energy to spin the engines. At low cruising speed, the engines require a minimum of heat (power) to turn at their maximum speed. But now their energy is being drained and the engines must have more heat. The

robot brain automatically increases the flow of fuel to the engines. The fuel pours into the engines at a much faster rate. The engine now operates at higher temperatures than it did before. The higher temperatures mean more power for the engines and the process continues.

The chain that links the power system can then be easily understood. The engines burn fuel to produce heat, and they convert this heat into the spinning motion of the engines. The spinning motion of the engines is transferred through the driveshaft to the gear reduction systems. These systems transfer power to turn the propellers. But they ration the amount of power that is transferred. It is as if the robot brain decided, "This is enough power for cruising speed. When you want more power, just shift the pitch of your blades."

The pilot advances the throttle, the gear system feeds more power to the propellers by draining power from the engines, the engines get more power by burning more fuel.

The C-130A model has engines that produce 3,750 horsepower. The new Hercules models, from the B through the E, have engines that deliver 4,050 horsepower. The engines have been so successful that over a period of ten years they have been increased in power by only 300 hp each. For the period of a decade, that is not much at all.

One model T56, already close to production,

operates at a higher temperature than the present engines. That increase in heat means an engine of 4,850 horsepower—or more than 3,000 horsepower extra per airplane.

And then, just a little further along in time, is the T56-M9 model which will deliver 5,980 horsepower.

Twenty-two thousand horsepower in the Hercules! One Hercules pilot thought of all that power and said: "Why, we'd get off the ground in just about five hundred feet!"

IN THE COCKPIT 5

TWENTY-FIVE thousand feet over Southeast Asia, an Air Force Hercules transport droned toward its destination. Everything was routine. The airplane slipped through the skies at nearly 350 miles per hour. In the cargo hold a massive bulldozer rested on the metal floor. Chains and cables lashed it solidly in place.

Then disaster struck without warning. No one knows to this day what happened, but the Hercules abruptly ran wild. The nose dropped in a violent maneuver, and the big transport screamed earthward.

Before the stunned crew could react, the airplane continued over into a straight vertical dive. Then the nose began to "tuck under" in the dive. This was the beginning of a high-speed outside loop. It would tear any airplane, including the Hercules, or the strongest fighter ever built, to jagged pieces.

The crew worked frantically to regain control. They didn't even know how fast they were diving. But it was well above the maximum speed for which the Hercules had been tested. The airspeed indicator had swung all the way around and was meaningless. The wind shrieked past the nose of the Hercules like a demon with a thousand voices. Buffeted by tremendous forces, the Hercules shook wildly, thrumming, shaking, and buffeting from nose to tail.

For twenty thousand feet the Hercules plummeted from the sky.

Only 5,000 feet above sea level, no more than 2,000 feet above the ground, the crew brought the airplane out of its screaming dive.

It took quite some time for the crewmen to regain their composure. You don't make dives of twenty thousand feet in a propeller airplane every day!

No one knew if the Hercules would continue to fly, or if it would fall apart at any moment. It vibrated, and the vibration grew worse. But the crew stayed with the Hercules, though their instinct was to bail out. They knew that by all the engineering rules ever written, the airplane should have torn apart in the dive.

The pilot kept lowering his forward speed, and at about 145 miles per hour the vibration disappeared.

At the first major airfield within reach, the pilot brought the Hercules to earth.

As soon as it stopped, the flight engineer went out to look at the damage. He wanted to find the source of the vibration. His excited shouts brought the rest of the crew.

"Will you just look at that . . ." The rugged metal fairing that covered the huge gear housing had been ripped completely away from the airplane. The side of the Hercules had been peeled like a grape, and the skin all the way up to the wing was gone. The ribs and structure of the airplane looked naked. The airplane seemed to have been raked by an enormous claw with steel nails.

The pilot didn't seem impressed. All he said was, "Yeah." The engineer stared at him. Then he turned to look in the direction where the pilot was pointing. The engineer gasped.

When the side fairing tore away in the dive, it had whirled crazily backward. The tremendous force of the wind had slammed it against the tail. Eleven feet of the right horizontal stabilizer was gone. The complete right elevator had vanished.

It was impossible. Any engineer could have told them that the Hercules (1) could not have survived the damage, and (2) that the airplane could not possibly have continued to fly.

But all that the crew had known was that at more than 145 miles per hour, the airplane vibrated.

Big airplanes are designed to be flown with skill and caution. They are not designed for abuse and punishment. Most airplanes equal in size to the Hercules would have been ripped apart by the 20,000-foot dive, especially with a bulldozer in the cargo deck.

One reason why the Hercules can take so much punishment is the superb "structural integrity" of the wings and body.

Under normal operating conditions, the Hercules wing has a structural integrity of 3g. This means that the airplane can be maneuvered safely even though the force of gravity on the wing is tripled. And this is under maximum weight conditions.

A 200-pound man under a 3g force weighs 600 pounds. The force of gravity is exerted on every part of his body, and he can barely move his arms. It is as though his limbs have turned to lead and his muscles are paralyzed. In this case we are referring to a 3g positive force. Positive g means that the force is exerted downward, in a line from the top of the head toward the feet. An airplane experiences positive g when it pulls out of a dive. The wings bend upward, straining against the tremendous pressure. In rough air, turbulence makes the effect even worse. Many airplanes have had their wings torn off in 3g pullouts.

But even worse than positive g is negative g. The direction of the force is reversed (upward from the feet toward the head). Airplanes do not stand up well to negative g pressures. An airplane is designed to fly so that the wings oppose gravity and support the weight of the airplane. They can flex upward to help fight positive g forces, but the negative g force is extremely damaging to the wings of big airplanes.

Flying the Hercules in negative g tests took great skill, courage, and endurance. When an airplane flies in level flight, it is under a force of 1g positive. To get to negative g, the pilot must go through a particular maneuver. The airplane is placed in a dive. Then the pilot pulls out of the dive. He uses his great speed to soar up and over in a huge arc. He becomes weightless. During the arc, the upward centrifugal force of the flight balances exactly the downward pull of gravity. After zero g (weightlessness), the pilot must push the controls forward to reach negative g.

Airliners are designed to withstand 1g negative. Their failing point, the absolute maximum they can take, is 1.5g negative. But pilots consider a force of 1g negative damaging to an airplane.

When the Hercules first took to the air, test pilots began a long program of learning everything they could about the airplane. Engineering tests, electronic computers, and experiments in wind tunnels can go only so far. The only way to know just what an airplane will do, what it can take, and how it will act is to fly that airplane.

The g-forces tests on the Hercules were wild. I have been through extreme g forces many times in military airplanes. Flying F-100F fighters with the Air Force, I have blacked out completely (7g). And I once went to a little more than 2g negative for several seconds. The negative forces send the blood pounding up to your head. Your veins bulge and it feels as though your head is going to burst. It is, to put it mildly, very unpleasant!

Test Pilot Leo Sullivan ran extensive experiments with the Hercules. During the negative g tests, the

Hercules would swoop up and over, and enter weightlessness. Here Leo Sullivan perfected his little game of the "weightless cigar." When the airplane reached full zero g, he opened his mouth and allowed his cigar to float gently away from his face. The trick was to let the cigar drift slowly. Then, when the airplane came out of its swooping arc, Sullivan would casually stretch out his arm. He would grasp the cigar easily in his fingers, and as the gravity forces built up, it would be back between his teeth.

Some of the Lockheed test pilots flew so many of these flights that they had more total time under weightlessness than did Astronauts Shepard and Grissom in their suborbital space flights!

There was a sequel to these tests that occurred several years later. The Hercules had proved extremely stable through these punishing flight maneuvers. Its huge fuselage made it an easy task to install experimental space equipment, so for several years now the Air Force has been training its Dyna-Soar space pilots in the Hercules. They practice maneuvers and special tests while they are weightless, as the Hercules soars up and over in its great arc through the sky.

Over and over again the pilots dove, zoomed, and racked the transports through maneuvers. Leo Sullivan explained:

"You go through a structural program of maneuvers that no one in his right mind would get into, except that in this business you must prove that the aircraft will fly through all its design limitations, and sometimes more. And you *can't* . . . do this either sitting on the ground or with daredevils in the air.

"We work with maximum instrumentation. We string gauges out on those wings, and we telemeter [transmit by radio] our data to the ground. The best people in this business are on the ground monitoring those instruments. They read off the results of what we're doing in the air. . . . We build up to maximum possible loads on the airplane slowly. We go to eighty, then ninety, and finally to one hundred per cent of what we are trying to do to prove the integrity of this machine.

"Every airplane built has its breaking point. I don't care if you built it to fly from grass fields or go to the moon, it will take just so much and no more."

The Hercules, during these flight tests, was limited to a maximum weight of 155,000 pounds. Leo Sullivan took a Hercules up at this weight, and pushed it into a dive. The transport plunged faster and faster until the wind shrieked wildly. Then, carefully, Sullivan began the punishing pullout from the dive.

At the bottom of the arc, the Hercules was enduring a force of three times normal gravity. At that moment, at 3g, the airplane weighed 465,000 pounds.

From the inside looking out . . . a crewman watches the heavy platform of a C-130 loaded with supplies whisk out from the hold. Notice the parachute that pulls the platform from the airplane; the main chutes haven't opened yet. (*Lockheed-Georgia*)

For one series of flight tests, the engineers modified the systems of the airplane. Apparently something went wrong, for the landing gear wouldn't come down; not even the backup system helped. The emergency system lowering the gear by manual controls failed too.

The emergency provided a dramatic demonstration of how strong the Hercules really was. The pilot had to make a wheels-up belly landing. He sank to the concrete of the runway with a terrifying screech of metal. When he finally ground to a halt, friction with the concrete had torn a big hole right down the center of the belly.

The crew raised the Hercules on jacks, and then lowered the gear. They put a strip of aluminum down the center of the airplane belly to hold the loose pieces in place, and took off from North Carolina and flew nonstop to Marietta, Georgia, for repairs. Four days later, as good as new, the Hercules was back in the air.

The Hercules is a *working* airplane. Therefore its tests required far more than precision flight and punishing maneuvers. The Hercules performs a wide variety of utility missions such as dropping trucks, armored vehicles, supply packages, tanks, and other massive loads from the air.

Before the Air Force accepted the Hercules, the Lockheed pilots had to prove that the transport could do anything asked of it. And that meant a major series of airdrop tests with heavier and heavier loads.

"The purpose of the tests," explains Leo Sullivan, "was to determine scientifically the capabilities of the airplane under extreme forces of flight. We did these tests with many instruments recording everything that went on. We had to determine the structural capability of the airplane in performing the airdrop missions."

The Air Force wanted to be able to drop by parachute a single load that weighed 28,000 pounds. Massive road graders of this weight were the test vehicles. The Air Force believed that fourteen tons would be the limit for a package dropped from the C-130.

They were wrong. The Hercules dumped the 28,000-pound loads without any trouble. And then it began to break every world record ever made for airdrops including its *own*.

The pilot slows the plane down to a speed of 140 to 170 miles per hour. He must control surfaces so that it will maintain its altitude even if he takes his hands from the controls.

The big cargo load booms out of the airplane. At the rate it whips free of the Hercules' cargo hatch, it takes only two to four seconds to leave the airplane. The speed of this cargo release is important. The time is so brief the airplane does not have much chance to react violently to the sudden massive shift and change in weight. Thus it avoids the severe pitching maneuver, a wicked rearing of the nose.

TRANSITION

As the Hercules flight test program continued, both Lockheed and the Air Force were pleased at the reports from the test pilots.

Yet the really critical test still had to be passed. Even though the airplane proved out its great strength and many other factors, it was doing so under the hands of skilled test pilots, who can fly almost anything.

What would happen when the regular Air Force transport pilots and crews moved into the Hercules? Not the test pilots or picked crews, but the men who flew the operational missions of the Air Force.

Jack Gilley, who was the Chief Flight Engineer of the testing program, insisted that special preparations be made to train the Air Force crews. The Hercules was a complex airplane compared to smaller twin-engine transports. The extreme range of its missions required an intensive transition and break-in period.

Lockheed was to train crews, for example, whose total experience was with the C-119. This is a twin-engine, low-level, unpressurized, fairly slow, and completely conventional piston-engine airplane. From the C-119 they were to begin flying the mighty Hercules.

Frankly, Lockheed was concerned about the problems that had to be overcome.

What happened was almost unbelievable. One of the top Lockheed pilots told the writer:

"We are still a little dazed with the spectacular success we had in transitioning to the Hercules. We had, without exception, complete success in moving the first Air Force pilots and crews into this airplane. The Air Force had studied the records of their previous experience and gave us some forbidding predictions. They said that during the eary transitioning of any big airplane, at least two or three planes would be wiped out.

"But it didn't happen. We came out of that program without even a single serious accident. And that stands as the greatest testimonial of all to the Hercules."

ASSAULT! 6

AS WE HAVE seen, every pilot who flew the Hercules during its development program was enthusiastic about it.

But, and it was a very important but, how would the Hercules perform as a weapon? How would it stand up to the grueling punishment of operations in the field? How would it endure handling by inexperienced crews? How would it make out without proper maintenance?

The only way to find out is to beat the daylights out of the airplane. In other words, take it out into the rough-operations areas, and turn the pilots loose.

This is the acid test. It produces situations as bad, and most likely worse, than those that will be encountered in actual operations. In these assault tests, the crews look for trouble, and go out of their way to find it. Their purpose is to stretch the airplane to its limit, and then go beyond it. The time to discover weaknesses and faults is not after the airplane is operational in large numbers. Problems must be rooted out at the beginning, and eliminated at once. This is known as working out the bugs.

One of the toughest field suitability tests was to operate the airplane from rough, short fields. Some of the greatest airplanes built become helpless in rough fields of grass, mud, sand, gravel, and dirt. The field may be bumpy and filled with ruts. Even the light airplane known as the puddle jumper bogs down under these conditions.

The Air Force has certain definitions for landing areas. A field that is crudely leveled is known as a hastily prepared runway. It is rough, but it has received some attention. When the Hercules first moved onto these hastily prepared fields, the Air Force demanded that the aircraft operate at a weight of 108,000 pounds. The assault transport passed these tests.

That was early in 1957. The Air Force then decided it needed greater performance, and demanded further tests. An assault transport must be able to do what is virtually impossible. It must be able to fly men and equipment not only to hastily prepared strips, but also to rough and unprepared terrain.

At Eglin Air Force Base in Florida there is a torture rack for airplanes. The terrain has been deliberately mangled so that it inflicts severe punishment on any airplanes that use it.

In one series of tests, they loaded the Hercules to weights of 102,000 to 110,000 pounds. Inside the flight deck the groans of the men could be heard above the crashing of the airplane and the cry of the engines, as the crew was shaken and buffeted. The wheels sliced huge furrows, a foot deep, in the ground.

The average airplane could not have moved without a few bulldozers to drag it free. But the Hercules crashed onto sandy fields, and slammed to a stop in 947 feet. Weighing 110,000 pounds and operating from the treacherous sand, the Hercules averaged a roll of only 1,500 feet before booming into the air.

The Air Force engineers now built an emergency field, and laid strips of pierced steel planking on the ground. They ordered the Hercules loaded to 116,000 pounds. Once again, the big transport was pronounced a success.

The Air Force laid down new specifications. The worst was for a complete simulated combat mission. The Hercules must slam onto a rough and unprepared strip. Then it must taxi across the treacherous ground to the side of the field, and pick up a cargo load of 25,000 pounds. Weighing 108,000 pounds, the Hercules must now take off in a short distance, fly 500 miles to another rough field. It must land with the heavy weight, and unload the cargo. Then, without refueling, it must fly 500 miles back to the first field.

When the crews finished the tests, the Air Force engineers were astounded. The Hercules had met every requirement. And then, they added another four tons of cargo to the airplane—and it passed all the tests again with an overload of 8,000 pounds.

Lockheed test pilot, Vern Peterson, who flew with

Bob Brennan (flight engineer), explained what the tests were like:

"The first day we arrived at Eglin, we took a jeep and rode up and down the field where we and the other crews were supposed to land the airplanes. What a place! There were piles of deep, soft sand everywhere you went. To make matters worse, wild brush sprouted haphazardly all about the sand.

"Jeeps were sinking deep into the sand, and some of them got stuck. And here we were getting set to fly airplanes through this stuff at weights up to 116,000 pounds! I do not mind telling you that we were a little perturbed about that field.

There were obstacles added to the field. We worked from a strip about 4,000 feet long. That was more than enough for the Hercules. But on each end of the field there were trees. And to make the test more difficult, the Air Force put up a 50-foot-high obstacle directly on the end of the runway. They stuck up two high poles and strung a wire with bright flags between the poles, so we wouldn't run into the wire."

Peterson and Brennan did taxi tests. The ground was so rough that the Hercules rocked back and forth in wild fashion. It acted like a small boat in a storm. But it moved up and down that field, it never got stuck, and it didn't suffer any damage.

They ran down the field at different speeds. They tested the power of the engines under different conditions. They slammed into obstructions and hard spots. The nose gear came screeching up as far as it would go and pounded with thundering blows against the bottom of the airplane.

"Right in the middle of this 'runway,' " Peterson said, "there was a hard road that cut across our path. We came booming down along the sand and whanged into this road, and BANG! we thought for sure the gear was going to come up right into the flight deck with us. We ran up and down until we reached about 90 miles per hour, holding the airplane on the ground, and then we stopped.

"During our first exposure to the takeoffs and landings, we were absolutely convinced that we were going to tear to shreds the whole front of the airplane. The shock forces are fantastic. It just didn't seem that anything could stay together under that beating. But after a while, and we were amazed by it, things settled down and became routine!"

During the final five days of the tests, at 116,000 pounds, the Hercules sank deeper than 20 inches into the sand. The gear doors that cover the wheels in flight, and extend downward for landing, were dragging six

A Navy Hercules takes off from Antarctica. The Hercules is the biggest airplane ever to wear skis. It makes shorter takeoffs and landings with much heavier loads than any other ski-equipped plane in the world. (*U.S. Navy*)

inches deep into the sand, yet there wasn't even a sign of structural damage.

Air Force flight crews repeated the tests. The results were the same. The Hercules was more than meeting every demand of the Air Force.

There were other tests, and at different locations. Some Hercules went far north. The crews flew in the worst of winter weather and in violent storms. They thundered through deep snowdrifts, skidded on gleaming ice, and fought their way, with engines howling, into the air from deep snow. Engineers laid steel planking down on swampy ground, and the Hercules splashed wildly onto the planking. Splashed is the right word—the airplanes almost disappeared from sight as they hurled sheets of water and mud all about them.

The airplanes flew over oceans, mountains, deserts

and through storms. Crews worked in shifts to slam the airplanes around. The Air Force did its best to wear out Hercules No. 12. Crews marched in and out of the airplane. During one period of two days—the airplane was in the air for 41 hours! One Lockheed engineer sent a telegram back to the big plant in Georgia: "Number Twelve is wearing out the crews as fast as the Air Force can supply them. Please send lots of stay-awake pills."

The Air Force made many flights that taxed the Hercules to its absolute design limit, and then went beyond this limit. The purpose of the tests was to determine critical stress loads.

One crew soared to 30,000 feet. There they put the airplane through a series of maneuvers for which it was designed. Then they went a bit further.

At six miles high, a pilot dropped the landing gear. The flaps slid down from the wings. The propeller blades shifted pitch. Then the pilot dumped the nose, shoving the airplane into a steep nose-down attitude. This was to be a "jet penetration." In this maneuver the airplane plunges from the sky but the forward speed is held back. One pilot reported what it was like:

"A jet penetration in the '130 will give you a thrill the first time you experience it. Much more so than a jet-fighter descent. Probably this is because of both the attitude of the plane, and the physical sensation. Frankly, it feels as though you were going to fall right through the front picture windows. We didn't accurately check the angle of dangle, but with the gear down, flaps full down, and throttles back, you'll find yourself standing on the rudder pedals. The rate-of-climb indicator shows 4,000 feet per minute down but, surprisingly enough, the airspeed is only 167 miles per hour."

And that is less than the landing speed of modern jet fighters and bombers.

The Hercules had proved itself out in rough fields, but the Air Force wanted more experience in short rough fields. How would the Hercules do in STOL (Short Takeoff and Landing) tests?

One Hercules, flown by Jesse Allen, began a gypsy tour. It bounced and roared from one field to another.

"We had some pretty wild touchdowns," Allen recalls. "More than once we saw stars from the impact. It felt like the nose gear was going to come right up through the floor."

The rough fields also tested the special Hercules wing. It is a wet wing, but it is also a flexible wing. It is supposed to bend up and down under severe stress. How much flexing, bending, and distortion could it take?

"We landed just about everywhere," Allen explains. "Many of the places had drainage ditches and holes you couldn't see. You never found out they were there until you hit those things with all the force of slamming right into a stone wall.

"Funny . . . but the landing gear seems to take the landings better than did the crews. The jolt is impossible to describe. . . . We would hit some fields with the main gear and it seemed as though the airplane would tear itself to pieces. The hammering and vibration was so bad you literally couldn't see clearly. And when that happened, you just whacked those levers forward and the bird was back in the air. That's when you appreciated that 'instant power' . . ."

The Hercules was spectacularly successful in rough-field operations. Air Force veterans tore up the old rule books and wrote new ones based on the Hercules' performance. Lockheed's decision to go to the high-wing design for the C-130 had proved itself. In the exceptionally rough fields, the airplane rocked wildly from side to side. It jolted along with all the motion of a sick whale, yet the bottom arc of the propeller tips were still about six feet off the ground. Otherwise, the props would have been chewing into dirt, stones, and other debris.

Another factor was equally important. The whirling blades of an airplane, especially one as powerful as the Hercules, create a tremendous suction. This is strong enough to snatch up rocks, wood, sand, and other objects. They can strike an airplane with enough force to cause serious damage. In the Hercules, this didn't happen, because the propellers were far from the ground.

The Hercules had plenty of get up and go. Everyone was delighted with its great speed of more than 370 miles per hour. But how slow could the airplane fly? This is important for short-field operations, and for special combat maneuvers.

Weighing 116,000 pounds, the C-130A was able to rumble through the air at just about 100 miles per hour. The Hercules pilots flew more and more slowly until they nearly reached this speed. They know they are close to a stall when the wings lack the lift to keep the airplane in level flight. The stall warning horns in the airplane blared continuously, but the Hercules just kept rumbling along under full control.

The flexible wing of the Hercules was a startling innovation for a propeller transport. In rough air it reduced "hunting" in turbulence. Hunting is the tendency of the nose to yaw from side to side. The wing also smoothed out the sharp gusts in rough air.

That wing was one of the most tortured parts of the Hercules. "You ever watch kids bouncing on the end of a long diving board?" asked an Air Force engineer. "First one kid goes out and he jumps up and down as hard as he can. Pretty soon the board is vibrating like a bowstring. This is so much fun he calls his gang, and then there are three or four kids out there. The board is groaning like an old bandsaw. If the lifeguard gets there in time, he may save the board before it breaks. If it is a really good board, however, it won't break."

The engineer laughed. "That's what we do with the

wing of the Hercules," he said. "We ask Lockheed to do the tests, but we look over their shoulder and kibitz. And our kids weigh each several hundred pounds. They're made of lead."

The Lockheed engineers turned one Hercules into a Lead Sled. They stacked tons of lead onto the wings. They suspended lead blocks from the engines, to simulate the violent stresses of turbulent flight. Then they put giant power clamps on the wings. They bent the wings up and down. And then they twisted and warped the wings at the same time!

The wings were battered and beaten until no one believed they could stay in one piece. The wingtips fluctuated and fluttered like pieces of rubber. One such test ran like this for fourteen hours. The engineers ran the Hercules through more than 200 fierce bending and twisting loads.

When it was all over, an engineer informed a Hercules test pilot that the wing had proven itself out completely. It was stronger than required—much stronger. It would be able to take severe punishment from operating in rough fields.

Just back from tests at Eglin, the pilot glared at the engineer. "You're telling me?" he snarled.

STRIKE!   7

IT IS FOUR o'clock in the morning at Sewart Air Force
Base in Tennessee. Darkness brings relief from the summer heat that blisters the sprawling airbase during the
day. The pilots and crews of the fleet of Hercules transports assigned to Sewart AFB are enjoying their first
pleasant sleep in many days.

Most of the base is asleep. Light glows dimly from
the control tower. Multicolored lights sail out of the
night and skim to a stop along the runway—a Hercules
crew are practicing night flying, takeoffs and landings.

In the operations room, in the office of the flight
dispatcher, and in security and meteorology offices men
are at work. Guards walk slowly along the flight line.
In more than one sprawling hangar mechanics are
working the night through on instruments, electronic
equipment, and all parts of the big transports. At a remote edge of the field, thrumming sounds rise and fall
as mechanics check out the Allison engines and the
propeller systems of other C-130's.

In yet another part of the base there stands a separate group of Hercules transports. These airplanes are

primed and cocked to go. They are part of the immedi-
ate-alert force. The tanks are filled. Everything is in
readiness for almost instant departure.

At 13 minutes past four A.M., the "red telephone"
rings. It is a combat alert—maximum deployment effort
for the Hercules. Few people realize that the crews of
the Tactical Air Command, who man the transports,
fighters, bombers, tankers, and other planes of TAC,
live under the same kind of alert as do the bomber
crews of the Strategic Air Command.

When the alert comes, telephones ring shrilly in the
crew quarters. It takes about five minutes for the men
to be out of bed, in their flying gear, and to have their
belongings rammed into personal flight bags. Every
man always keeps a bag at his side for such an emergency. He may be gone for many weeks, and he will
have to live out of that bag.

The pilots move at once to flight operations. Here
they receive details of the alert call, what it means, what
it will require. Navigators are already checking the
routes. Instead of going through the elaborate process
of preparing their flight plans, they take from their
flight cases special plans that were made up months
before. They keep them up-to-date, noting all changes
of radio frequencies, routes, and other data. Once the
navigator sees the destination, he'll use the preplanning
flight charts. He may have to modify them slightly, but
he won't need to spend hours at this work. He is ready
to go.

The copilots check with the meteorology office. What's the weather for takeoff, for the first landing area? How is it en route? How is it now, and what will it be later? How about the destination? What are the clouds, any storm conditions?

Orders have come down through a series of commands to Sewart Air Force Base and the crews of the Hercules transports. Involved in this elaborate chain of command are units of all the armed services. Everything functions smoothly. There have been many practice runs, tests and drills to achieve that perfection. Outstanding performance is never an accident. It is the result of careful planning and exhaustive practice.

No one knows whether the alert is a drill, or the real thing. The crews have learned the hard way that it is impossible to tell one from the other. In 1958 they were called out on alert, just as they are now. They were certain it was just one more practice. But some of those crews didn't return to Sewart Air Force Base for two months.

They were on duty in the Middle East. War had threatened to break out in Lebanon, when the president of that country found Communist groups trying to overthrow his government. On the border, Russian tanks and armored forces were lining up. The moment the Communist uprising was successful, the Communists would "invite" the Russians into Lebanon. Lebanon would become another helpless satellite of the Communist domain.

The President of Lebanon appealed to the United States for help. Our nation responded swiftly and with great strength. The key to this operation was a new organization known as CASF—the Composite Air Strike Force.

The CASF was made of different elements of the Tactical Air Command. B-57 jet bombers roared off from their TAC fields in the United States and headed for the Middle East. Immediately behind the bombers came squadron after squadron of powerful F-100 jet fighters. Even as the fighters boomed out of their fields, great tanker planes took off from Bermuda. The fighters and tankers rendezvoused over the Atlantic. The tankers released their long fuel hoses with drogues and the fighters moved in, and hooked up.

Later, other tankers flew from Lajes in the Azores for additional meetings to fuel the fighters. Some twelve hours after leaving the United States, the F-100's were on the ground in Adana, Turkey. Two hours after that the pilots were flying combat patrols.

They were the vanguard of a mighty striking force thundering toward Lebanon. Soon formations of 1,200-MPH Voodoos were in the air. RF-101A reconnaissance fighters swept at supersonic speed over enemy installations, their cameras recording every detail of the movements of the opposing forces.

RB-66A Destroyer weather-reconnaissance jet bombers raced toward the Middle East. The tankers met the

Voodoos and the Destroyers, and again the aerial fueling went off steadily.

Involved in that powerful force were many Hercules transports. The first wave carried skilled maintenance men, radar specialists, and technicians. In each airplane was a special Flyaway Kit with the essential tools and spare parts for the fighters and bombers of the CASF. The Hercules would enable the combat striking force to remain operational.

As the first group of Hercules departed for the Middle East, another force flew a short distance to Fort Bragg, North Carolina. Moving quickly over the ground, the airplanes lowered their ramps, and then swung into parking position. As soon as they stopped, long lines of paratroopers filed into the transport planes. Minutes later, the planes were lining up at the end of the runway. Then, one after the other, they roared into the air and headed for Lebanon.

This, then, is the CASF—the Composite Air Strike Force of the Tactical Air Command. On this particular morning, the Hercules crews are told to fly quickly to the paratrooper base in North Carolina. That is all they are told. The paratroopers move into the planes, the transports rumble down the runways and into the air. The pilots follow the course that has been given them.

Fifteen minutes later the word comes true. It is not an actual alert. Today's mission is one of practice. Observers watch everything that happens. They note any problems that slow down the operations. The Hercules fly to a practice area, where the paratroopers bail out on a simulated combat mission. Then the airplanes land at a nearby field. In the evening they fly the weary combat troopers back to Fort Bragg.

The Composite Air Strike Force has become one of America's mightiest weapons for preventing a war. Very few Americans know about the CASF, how it came into being, and what it does. To understand this vital element of American power, we must briefly examine the development of powerful weapons in recent years.

After World War II, both the United States and the Soviet Union pressed the development of three major weapons. One was the long-range, or strategic, bomber. Both the United States and the Russians built a powerful striking force of bombers. There was no question, however, that our Strategic Air Command was much more powerful than that of the Soviet Union. We had more bombers; they were bigger, and they were considerably faster. Even more important, the United States had great experience in long-range bomber operations. We had flown massive forces in World War II all through Europe, the Mediterranean, and Russia. In the Pacific, our giant B-29's were flying missions of over 3,500 miles against Japanese targets.

The Russians were behind, but they were catching

up fast. It was only a matter of time until both nations had great strategic bomber fleets. Then, it would not matter whether one plane was slightly faster or bigger than the other.

The second major weapon was the nuclear bomb. In 1945 the United States ended World War II by dropping atomic bombs on Hiroshima and Nagasaki. The Japanese surrendered, the first time in history that a great nation had been defeated without an invasion.

By 1949 the Soviet Union exploded its first atomic bomb. By 1954 both the United States and Russia had successfully tested the hydrogen bomb. During the next several years both countries exploded these bombs in test after test. They placed in production bombs that were equal in power to 20,000,000 to 50,000,000 tons of TNT. (The bombs today are more powerful than 100,000,000 tons of TNT.)

The third major weapon is the intercontinental ballistic missile (ICBM). The Russians tested their first ICBM in the summer of 1957. By the following year the United States and the Soviet Union were working frantically to develop these giant rockets.

For the last several years both countries have produced mighty ICBM forces. The United States has placed Atlas, Titan I, Titan II, and Minutemen missiles in deep silos beneath the ground. Only a direct hit could hope to damage or knock out such a silo. And there are hundreds of them.

We have placed nuclear submarines far at sea. Each submarine carries 16 Polaris missiles. Like the ICBM's, each Polaris has a powerful nuclear warhead.

The Soviet Union has also placed missiles underground, and sent big submarines to sea with other missiles.

In addition to the missile forces, both nations have their mighty bomber fleets. Each has thousands of smaller jet bombers, and fighters that can carry nuclear bombs. Each has medium-range missiles, short-range missiles, and the means of delivering these weapons.

As a result, both nations have a tremendous overkill capability. They have enough power to destroy each other completely a thousand times over. Trying to solve international problems with nuclear attacks, then, really solves nothing at all. It destroys targets, cities, and perhaps entire nations.

We have arrived at what the military experts call a nuclear stalemate. We have counterinvulnerability. Neither dares to attack the other because each is so powerful. And the weapons of each country can survive any initial attack. No matter what happens to the attacked country, it will be able to react with its own devastating nuclear blow.

Nobody can win such a war.

Faced with the nuclear stalemate, the Communists have turned to other means for increasing their control—limited and guerrilla warfare, such as the battles fought in Korea and Indochina.

Many years before these battles came to an end, the Tactical Air Command recognized the need for a new type of war capability. TAC's leaders saw clearly that massive strategic forces could do the United States little good in the limited and guerrilla wars of the Communists. No one wanted to fight the big war, so our missiles and hydrogen bombs were of no use in the brushfire wars that sprang up whenever the Communists decided to start more trouble.

We needed a new concept of airpower to meet the Communists on their own terms. The Communists would always be able to select the time, the place, and the method of battle. Subversion was their way. But when the brushfire wars broke out, we would have to respond in such strength that the war would end quickly. What would be even better was to prevent such wars. To do this, we needed a powerful striking force based in the United States.

It would consist of fighters, bombers, maintenance forces, reconnaissance and intelligence services. It must have a swift means of transporting crack fighting men to the source of trouble. Our military experts began to work carefully to build that force. They knew that if they were successful, we could let the Communists call the time and place, and we could whip them at their own game.

Two separate avenues were followed. The first was to create a new type of logistics-assault machine on wings. It would have to be an airplane with tremendous performance and versatility, capable of both high and low speeds, and with a long range. It must be extremely reliable, and be able to operate out of rough and unprepared fields. It must carry cargo in the fashion of a freight train, and yet fly faster than our fighter planes of World War II.

This go-anywhere, any-place, any-time airplane is none other than the Hercules. It was created to meet the needs not of one military service but of the United States. It was to be the assault and logistics weapon that would help us to defeat the Communists in any trouble they decided to start.

TAC began a special series of tests to prove the worth of its plan for a composite air striking force. It must be based in the United States, and be able to strike quickly at any point in the world. To keep massive fighting units everywhere in the world in the event of trouble would require 10,000,000 men under arms, and a budget almost as big as that for fighting World War II. Not even the United States could afford that.

In 1951, TAC deployed a force of fighters, bombers, and troop-carrier planes to Europe in the first series of tests. They tested combat methods, airlift, and other military tactics. But the units of TAC were not yet strong. TAC had to call upon other Air Force commands for help. The TAC deployments were not made as a show of strength but were intended to ferret out weaknesses and show where strength was needed. This was the slow and careful forging of a new weapon that is an entire striking force itself.

TAC now experimented with aerial refueling, which is the key to mobility with strength.

In May, 1954, TAC carried out Exercise BOXKITE, which tested many of the theories of the CASF. It proved the need for austere and rugged techniques in operations.

The tests came faster. Exercise FLASHBURN saw the powerful TAC troop carrier force, plus other Air Force transports, in a massive airlift. Nearly 600 transports airlifted more than 9,000 combat troops. The troop carrier airplanes also dumped 216,000 pounds of cargo in nine seconds into the combat zone.

On August 27, the first test Hercules took to the air, and in September TAC received its first supersonic jets. Delivery of the rugged F-100 Super Sabre fighters and fighter bombers gave TAC one of the deadliest weapons ever built. Within two years the new F-100C fighters were in service. They could refuel with aerial tankers and gave TAC true global mobility.

By 1958 TAC was equipped with KB-50J tankers, which used four powerful piston engines and two jet engines to gain high speed for refueling the jet fighters and bombers. With the KB-50J's came supersonic RF-101 Voodoo reconnaissance fighters that could hit 1,200 miles per hour.

In 1957 the troop carrier units received their first

Hercules transports. But it would be some time yet before the C-130's were part of TAC's major airlift force. It takes time to train pilots and crews. Maintenance men must become familiar with the airplane. Above all, the airplane must be used on actual maneuvers with Army and Air Force units, to prove its value.

Anticipating the arrival of the Hercules, TAC in 1955 created the unique 19th Air Force. Unlike TAC's two other forces, the 9th and 12th Air Forces, the 19th faced a monumental challenge. First, it had no airplanes. Its entire headquarters and operational staff numbered less than a hundred people.

Its mission was: "Be prepared to deploy any and all assigned units to any theater or area in the world as might be directed, and be capable of exercising operational control of attached units upon their arrival in the combat zone."

The Commander of the 19th, Major General Henry Viccellio, had been one of the prime architects of the Composite Air Strike Force. Now he was to make the concept a reality.

The CASF itself would be made up of planes and men from regular TAC units. Plans were laid down for every possible emergency. When a CASF was ordered into operation, Viccellio and his staff would blow the whistle. TAC units, prepared to respond immediately to any alarm, would come under his direct command.

General Viccellio stated the role of CASF:

"The very location of potential hot spots high-lights a special CASF characteristic. It is by nature complementary to other American forces . . . when the Soviets increase their pressure on remote hot spots, we must intensify our counter-measures with SAC, with far-ranging naval carrier forces in Europe and the Far East. This is our big stick concept in keeping things limited . . . versatility is to us far more than a glittering generality—it enables us to produce the exact degree of force at the right place at the right time."

That force could not be measured only in combat airplanes. The CASF teams moved out with devastating firepower at their control. The planes were fully equipped with a bristling array of weapons. They were prepared to move in fast and, if necessary, hit with terrifying power. They would not use nuclear weapons, although these were always kept ready and waiting should they be necessary. No one wanted even to think about their use, for the whole purpose of CASF was to limit a war. CASF was an international fire brigade to stop brush-fire wars.

To accomplish this purpose, the CASF must also consist of fighting men, who were extraordinarily skilled in combat techniques. They must be paratroopers, engineers, demolitions experts, and infantrymen.

And they had to be moved fast. This is where the Hercules came in.

As quickly as the first C-130's moved into the troop carrier units of TAC, they were subjected to grueling and realistic combat situations. When the tests ended, both TAC and the Army were jubilant. They had the greatest assault weapon ever known.

At Pope Air Force Base in North Carolina (as part of the early tests), ninety-two fully-equipped soldiers marched into the gaping hold of a Hercules. And we mean marched. No one climbed through doors or up steps. The men double-filed through the yawning rear cargo door of the airplane. Aboard the Hercules came special observers. With the crew, there were one hundred four men in the transport.

Thirteen minutes after takeoff the pilot leveled off

"Just line 'em up, march 'em in, fire up the engines—and *go.*" That's the procedure for carrying ninety-two fully-equipped men and their weapons in the capacious hold of the Hercules. (*Lockheed-Georgia*)

at 25,000 feet. At 360 miles per hour, he headed for the "combat area" 2,000 miles away. Inside the cavernous hold of the airplane the pressure remained constant at 9,000 feet-equivalent. Just outside the thick skin of the Hercules the temperature was 52° below zero—inside, it was an even 70°.

At the combat area, the Hercules plunged in a jet penetration. It roared over trees and thumped down onto a clay strip. Even as the pilot reversed the propellers and slammed on the brakes, the rear ramp slid down. The troops poured out quickly to establish an advanced battle base. The Hercules crew moved swiftly through the airplane. On the spot they converted it to a medical evacuation ship. Soon afterward the Hercules roared into the air with seventy-four "litter patients" and doctors aboard.

The test was spectacularly successful. The Air Force repeated it several times, noted the same outstanding performance, and chalked off one more item on the Hercules' "prove it" list.

Two Hercules' without prior alert were given an "emergency supply mission." Six hours later they completed delivery of 185 tons of ammunition, artillery weapons, varied supplies—and hundreds of combat-equipped troops. Each time they departed from the combat area they were filled to capacity with "wounded" and "litter patients."

The Hercules' transports roared into the paratrooper bases. They made mission after mission to disgorge the troops. Often they flew 1,200 miles before sixty-four men leaped from each airplane. The Army took pictures of more than 5,000 jumps under combat-simulated conditions.

When these tests ended, the only change they made in the Hercules was to install a windbreak by the side jump doors. This lowered the blast of air when the paratroopers leaped into space.

One Hercules thundered into a rough forward strip. Out of the assault transport came a huge truck, a 155-mm howitzer, and ten fully-equipped soldiers. The crew then loaded aboard seventy-four men on stretchers, plus medical attendants. The total time spent on the ground for unloading and loading, without shutting down the engines, was exactly thirty minutes.

What would happen in a real emergency? Suppose the airplane landed in a strip so short that it couldn't get out again, even with all its great power. Could the big Hercules use rocket boosters to "spring out" of the strip? Leo Sullivan made the test.

Sullivan ran the engines and props to maximum thrust. He then jumped the brakes, and the Hercules bolted forward. In just a few seconds it reached a speed of about 60 miles per hour. At that moment Sullivan triggered the eight rocket bottles. Brilliant flame spat from each side of the airplane, and a blast of thunder rocked the field. Almost as quickly as he ignited the rockets, Sullivan was hauling back on the wheel.

Less than 450 feet from the start of takeoff, the

Hercules leaped into the air. At an angle of 45 degrees, the big airplane shot into the sky. Twelve seconds after firing the rockets the Hercules was pulled by her Allisons alone, the empty bottles falling earthward.

In North Carolina a group of Hercules' roared over rough mountain country. The ramps came down. A bulldozer and then a shower of heavy construction equipment burst away from the planes. Parachutes cracked open and lowered them to earth.

Minutes later, three hundred thirty fighting men of the 101st Airborne Division's Engineer Battalion dropped into the wild country. The terrain abounds in rocks, trees, and is rugged. The paratrooper engineers worked around the clock. They hacked and gouged and scraped away at the stubborn earth. Just twenty-six hours after the first man opened his parachute, they were done. A rough strip 2,500 feet in length lay like a scar through the undergrowth.

Then dust billowed upward in great clouds. Hercules after Hercules pounded onto the strip, bringing in men, trucks, artillery, and armored vehicles.

In Alaska, for ten weeks the crews abused the airplane to see how it could withstand the rigors of the far north. They let the Hercules stand in cold 50° below zero. Then, without preheating the engines or performing any other service, they started the airplane and performed "emergency mission" departures.

The pilots deliberately ran off runways and thundered into high snowbanks. The Hercules looked sometimes like a huge bird whose wings were broken. It battered and snorted its way through drifts of snow. Great clouds of misty white blasted back from the snarling propellers. It broke free and roared into the air.

That Hercules flew a bewildering variety of missions. It carried troops, and dropped paratroopers. It dumped heavy equipment earthward. It proved it could handle anything.

Farther south, in Minnesota, another Hercules astounded the experts during Project SLIDE (Snow, Land and Ice Development Exercise).

This Hercules looked like a misfit—a huge three-runner bobsled on wings. It thumped and banged its way around all kinds of ice and snow on the biggest skis ever placed on an airplane.

What really amazed onlookers was the fact that even with its huge skis (they weighed 2,000 pounds each, and there were three of them), the Hercules operated from dry runways. The skis could retract while the gear was down, and thus expose the wheels. This test was especially important, as the Air Force needed a ski-equipped Hercules for a critical assignment.

Flying the ski-equipped Hercules (it later became the C-130D) was a wild operation. Ice ridges couldn't even be seen against blinding white. The airplane slammed into the ridges with pile-driver force. Even the huge skis and shock absorbers couldn't soften the blows that almost rattled the teeth of the crewmen.

Crosswinds drove the pilots to frenzied attempts to control the airplane. On its skis the Hercules weighs sixty tons. The wind always seemed to be blowing at a right angle to the machine. On a glass-slick surface the crosswind was an additional hazard.

But the Hercules proved more than equal to the task, and the Air Force declared the ski-equipped C-130D fully operational.

The Army engineers assembled 110 pieces of equipment to test the Hercules, and assigned 32 engineer outfits to the test program.

No one had planned to use the Hercules for transporting heavy construction equipment. But this was part of the assignment, and once again the airplane accomplished a new task with ease.

Engineers loaded sections of portable bridges into the Hercules. Within 15 seconds after the C-130's had come to a stop, the bridges were rolling out of the cargo hold.

The Hercules' delivered giant bulldozers weighing 36,000 pounds. They hauled portable asphalt plants, road graders and scrapers, heavy road rollers, crane cabs, excavators, tractors, and 35,000-pound trucks.

But how about really bulky cargo? Here, the Hercules proved itself, not in a test, but on assignment.

American forces in Adana, Turkey, sent an emergency request for a generator that weighed 28,700 pounds. It was a great hulking piece of machinery. The first attempt to airlift it with another transport failed.

"If there isn't a field around, and the surface is too rough—build the field. And do it fast!" That's the motto of airborne engineers, who jump from low-flying Hercules transports that also dump bulldozers, graders, steel planking and other equipment into rough country. (*U.S. Army*)

The Hercules was new to the 322nd Air Division. It was not operational, but was on training status. The emergency meant, however, that the Air Force had to try anything.

At Laon, France, they loaded the generator into the Hercules. The big Lockheed flew at an average speed of 346 miles per hour all the way to Adana—2,281 miles nonstop—in well under seven hours.

The final series of tests involved dropping bigger and heavier loads than had ever been carried by parachutes. Roadgraders, bulldozers, tractors, and other equipment sailed from the sky. Trucks, tanks, and artillery floated earthward. No matter what the Air Force brought into the Hercules, it handled the job.

The airplane broke every airdrop record ever made, and then broke its own records. In one flight alone, four new world records were set when six giant parachutes carried a 27,000-pound roadgrader safely to the earth.

A single Hercules in ripple-fire fashion heaved an M-55 gun mount, a 105-mm howitzer, and a jeep into the air. All three landed without damage. Minutes later another Hercules dumped a 19,000-pound roadgrader out of its cargo ramp, and then released a 40-mm gun mount weighing 7,500 pounds.

Then an airplane in England dropped a single load of 32,000 pounds. It swept the airdrop records away from the United States Air Force. The Royal Air Force transport was a—Hercules!

It didn't take long to bring the record back home. The sixth Hercules off the production line heaved a single load into the air that weighed 35,055 pounds. The record went to 40,500 pounds. Finally it reached 41,740 pounds—and there it stands today.

The Composite Air Strike Force had progressed from the planning stage to become the 19th Air Force. And the 19th Air Force proved that the planning had been sound, first in Lebanon, and several months later, when planes and fighting men were sent to the Pacific where the Chinese Communists were threatening to invade Formosa. Within the space of a few days the United States had built up a powerful striking force, and the threat evaporated.

But there were still serious problems. One of the most critical was the need to coordinate the work of the Air Force and the Army. Too much time was being lost in getting the planes and the fighting forces together.

The answer lay in another organization—the Strike Command (better known as STRICOM or STRIKE). The Strike Command, under General Paul D. Adams, was set up to integrate the Strategic Army Corps (STRAC) and TAC into a single unified command. In September of 1961 STRIKE was a reality.

The Strategic Army Corps—perhaps 150,000 fighting men and their weapons—is made up of two airborne divisions and one infantry division. These include the 82nd and 101st Air-borne divisions, and the 4th Infantry Division, and make up what is known as the XVIIIth Air-borne Corps.

I visited General Adams in his headquarters at Mac-Dill Air Force Base in Florida to ask him what STRIKE means in terms of our new power. He said that the basis of Strike Command's operations was "effective, selective, flexible, and rapid reaction." Then, he continued:

"I would like to emphasize that this means rapid reaction with the necessary force to accomplish the mission, or to move anywhere and execute a tactical operation with the minimum of preparation and orders."

I asked about the speed with which Strike Command can get into action. It is one thing for the Hercules transports to be on the spot, but what happens after the transports arrive at the Army centers?

"We maintain the Division Ready Force," General Adams said. "These troops are in the air-borne divisions and we rely on them for the immediate, quick move.

"They are on 'Division Ready Force Alert' twenty-four hours a day, without fail. During the period that the battle group is assigned to this mission, its first company must be ready to load all men and weapons within 90 minutes of a no-notice cold start.

"The rest of the force we require comes along as rapidly as the aircraft can come in. We make these moves in an 'air screen' column instead of a formation. The men move up and are prepared to load as we assemble the aircraft in the loading base.

"Then as that battle group moves out, or completes

On an actual combat alert, a force of Hercules transports prepares to pick up thousands of combat-ready troops. (*U.S. Air Force*)

its loading, the next battle group in the division is getting ready to start its out-loading.

"It's a one-behind-the-other sort of thing; a continuous flow. . . ."

Here is a new, powerful striking force, able to go anywhere, anytime. Its purpose: not simply to fight or to win wars, but to prevent them, by being so powerful that no one will want to take a risk against the strength of such a force.

At the heart of this force is the mighty Hercules.

MISSION TO EUROPE   **8**

A FLIGHT in the Hercules from the United States to southern Europe is an exciting experience. In the spring of 1963 I made that flight. The airplane was a C-130B Hercules of the 314th Troop Carrier Wing, attached to the 839th Air Division at Sewart Air Force Base, Tennessee. To her crew she was simply 297, the serial number painted in big black numbers on the side of the nose.

Our flight to Europe, like all flights in the Air Force, was for a specific purpose. There are more than one hundred Hercules transports assigned to the 839th Air Division. These airplanes are in constant use. There is always flight training to be done to keep crews fully qualified, and to check out new men assigned to the division. The transports fly support missions for the United States Army on a steady basis. Fort Bragg is near Sewart Air Force Base, as is Fort McCampbell, and the Hercules' move in a steady procession to and from the Army installations.

The Hercules' provide the airlift for troop maneuvers. They carry at least ninety-two fully-equipped

The front end of the Hercules is a great expanse of metal and glass. The black, bulbous shape houses complex electronic equipment and radar antenna. (*Photo by Hank Curth*)

soldiers on exercises in the field. When paratrooper attacks are simulated, each Hercules carries sixty-four men who will leap into space from the transport. Then there are the airdrops, when the Hercules drop howitzers, tanks, trucks, jeeps, cargo loads, and other military equipment.

The Air Force and the Army are constantly experimenting with new techniques and equipment.

As part of the Tactical Air Command, the 839th Air Division carries out missions as ordered by TAC Headquarters. These include personnel transportation, carrying cargo, and research.

All transports are always on an alert status. This means that the TAC crews live under a standby alert every day of the year. In the event that the airplanes are needed for emergency missions, they must be ready to move out almost immediately upon notice.

Each TAC squadron is required to serve at an overseas base for at least two duty assignments each year. Normally, they last ninety days, and then the crews return to the United States to resume their duties at Sewart AFB.

Each squadron flies to the military field of Evreux-Fauxville Air Base in France. Evreux is about 60 miles from Paris. The mission assignments keep the men moving almost constantly. They're on the go by day and night. Evreux is the home of the 322nd Air Division, part of our military air strength in Europe. The 322nd is equipped mainly with Hercules transports.

And this is our destination with Hercules 297. Our pilot, Major Wallick, and his crew are assigned to the 61st Troop Carrier Squadron. Now, it is this outfit's turn to spend three months on duty in France. The squadron now on duty there is returning to Sewart, and we will pass one another during the flights to and from Europe.

In the cargo hold of our airplane there are more than thirty airmen of the 61st Troop Carrier Squadron (TCS). The fuselage is crammed with the men's baggage. There are also crates and boxes filled with spare parts and equipment to maintain the Hercules.

We have a definite flight plan. We will leave Sewart Air Force Base in Tennessee and fly directly to Kindley Air Force Base in Bermuda. After remaining overnight, we will continue across the Atlantic to Lajes in the Azores. We will remain there overnight to give the crew a rest. On the following morning we will fly to Evreux-Fauxville Air Base.

Major Wallick and his crew carefully go through the pretakeoff checklist. As they do so, black clouds sweep low overhead. We are in the path of a series of heavy showers. One moment there is no rain. The next moment the sky seems to break and water pours down in torrents.

Lined up on the runway, Major Wallick locks the brakes and runs the power all the way to maximum thrust. The Hercules trembles and vibrates through every inch of her great structure. Major Wallick is unhurried and calm. He is a superb pilot with many years of experience, and he learned years ago the value of doing things the right way. Finally, he is satisfied.

He calls the control tower and announces that he is

starting to roll. All of us in the flight deck brace our-
selves. Major Wallick snaps the brakes free and Hercules 297 bounds forward. The airplane is loaded to just
about its maximum gross weight; with our heavy cargo
load and fuel, we are at about 135,000 pounds.

For the first 500 feet or so of the ground roll, Wallick
steers the airplane down the runway with a small wheel
mounted to his left. At low speeds, the great rudder is
still ineffective for directional control; it needs air flowing past it at high speed. Until that speed is reached,
the pilot directs the Hercules down the runway by
steering the big nose gear. When he turns the little
wheel, a hydraulic boost system moves the nose gear
wheels. But this lasts only seconds, and then the rudder
"grabs" the air. Wallick places both hands on the control yoke.

The Hercules is running fast now under full bore.
Wallick knows that the copilot and the flight engineer
are watching the gauges and instruments. His concern
is with the speed of the airplane and its control for
flight.

The Hercules can get up and go in a hurry. But pilots
use the assault takeoff only when that technique is
required.

When he reaches enough speed for the controls to
have full effect, he eases back on the control yoke. The
nose wheel lifts off the ground, and holds the airplane
in that same attitude. We rush down the runway, nose
pointed slightly up, our speed increasing with every

second. Then there comes that moment when the lift of the wings becomes greater than the weight of the Hercules. It is at that moment that the airplane eases away from the earth. It literally flies itself away from the ground in a movement that is absolutely smooth.

As soon as we are clear of the ground, the landing gear is retracted. Then the flaps slide back into the wings, and the airplane is cleaned up for flight.

We rush into the dark mists and clouds that hang low over the ground. Wallick is flying with scientific precision. He has forgotten the outside world. To him, the world is represented in the instruments on the panel before him. He guides the airplane by the readings of those dials. He studies airspeed, rate of climb, rate of turn, angle of bank. He watches an artificial horizon, a gyroscopic instrument that simulates the horizon of the earth. By watching the movements of a tiny airplane on that dial, he can tell exactly what the airplane is doing in relation to the real, or outside, world.

We know our exact position over the earth because of electronic devices. Powerful transmitters on the ground send signals that register on our instruments and tell us where we are and where we are heading. Then, we are also scanned by radar from the ground. Air traffic controllers are in constant touch with us. We follow their orders explicitly. There are many other airplanes in the sky, all of them flying IFR (Instrument Flight Rules). Each airplane is allotted a certain block of airspace.

As we speed along in climbing turns, the earth drops

lower and lower beneath us. And then comes one of the most wonderful moments in flight. We begin to break out of the clouds. The first glimpse of the outside world comes in the form of a brilliant shaft of sunlight. Somewhere above us the clouds have parted slightly. The beam of light spears down through the dark mists and we fly into its path.

With each passing second we continue to forge our way clear of the clouds. Now we are in the half-world of clouds and clear air. Our speed seems to be tremendous as we plunge from the swirling mists into clear air, and then knife again into the clouds. Soon we are skimming along the tops of the cloud mountains.

Several minutes later, the flashing speed of the airplane is gone. Now the clouds lie well below us as we level off at 25,000 feet. Five miles above the earth, Wallick trims the Hercules out for level flight. Our speed increases steadily as the big propellers chew at the air and build up momentum. The Hercules settles down finally at about 330 miles per hour cruising speed. It will continue to increase steadily as the jet engines steadily consume the thousands of gallons of kerosene in the wing tanks. With less weight the airplane automatically gains in its forward speed.

Now, with everything properly set up in the flight deck, Wallick works the controls to activate the automatic pilot. Seconds later he pushes his seat back, stretches his legs, and lights a cigarette. An electronic brain linked to spinning gyroscopes has taken over.

While we continue to fly, the crew monitors the instruments. But they do not need to touch a single control. The robot brain and pilot are attending to all this. The crew will take over the controls only if the electronic brain fails to perform perfectly.

The man who does the most work now is Captain Bowman. As navigator, he must keep a constant running check of the airplane's position over the earth. Flying across the United States, his task is made easier by the electronic transmissions of radio and radar from the ground. But once we cross the coast of the United States, we are over a vast expanse of ocean. For many miles the electronic highways of the sky will help guide us. But then there are miles of nothingness. Bowman has charts spread out on his navigator's table. He plots the position of the sun in the sky. He takes readings from one point to another of the celestial body. Then he spins small flight computers in his hand. He jots down figures and makes computations. He keeps track of our progress on his charts. He knows exactly our latitude and our longitude over the surface of the earth.

He has drawn a course line from the coastline of the United States to Bermuda. As we continue on our way, he plots our position. Every now and then he tells the pilot to change course by a few degrees. At our height the winds blow from different angles. There is no way to tell if we are drifting to the right or the left of our course. No way by looking, that is. But Bowman, with his instruments, his skill, and his computations, does know precisely what is happening.

We have a crosswind from our left; that means we must compensate for the sideward drifting effect of the wind. Major Wallick turns the nose of the Hercules several degrees to the left. The nose of the airplane is not pointed along our course, but to the left of it. The slight shift in our compass heading will cancel out exactly the effects of the crosswind. And we will continue along our way as planned.

Hours later the clouds have vanished. The Atlantic lies far below, its surface even from five miles high visibly whipped by the wind. We can see the white foaming spots of whitecaps—water boiling and surging as it rides up and down swells. There is no question but that the wind down there is fierce. The waves seem to be at least ten to twenty feet high.

Time passes. Finally, Bowman calls Major Wallick. The navigation instruments seem to have come alive, flickering for a moment. Then the needles snap straight and true. Many miles out, we are picking up the transmissions of the Air Force station at Bermuda. We are dead on beam.

The crew prepares for the long, sloping descent to Bermuda. Major Wallick eases the nose down slightly. There is no need to drop toward the earth in a rapid descent. We will take advantage of gravity as the Hercules slides gently out of the sky, the nose down only a few degrees. Our speed will increase slightly.

Then, on the horizon far ahead of us, we see a mass of clouds. The radar approach control at Kindley Air Force Base issues new instructions. The pilot is to increase his rate of descent, and level off only 1,000 feet above the ocean. We will come into Bermuda at this low height below the clouds. Instead of flying an instrument-controlled approach through the turbulence of the clouds, our flight will be "eyeballs all the way."

Low over the ocean, after its drop from altitude, the Hercules races toward Bermuda. The ocean is a deep, wonderful blue color. Bermuda lies ahead.

The landing gear comes down with a thump and a bang, the flaps slide out of the wings, and Wallick eases the big airplane toward the runway ahead of us. Hills rise steeply to our left as we descend more steeply now. Then, another stretch of water. Finally, the concrete runway flashes beneath the wings. Our speed falls slowly as Wallick holds the nose of the Hercules up, holding the airplane in the air, and letting it settle by itself. There comes a subdued screech behind us as the massive tires skim the runway. We are down, the first leg of our fight completed.

ON TO SPAIN

We stayed in Bermuda for two evenings. Our plans were to take off the morning after our arrival for Lajes in the Azores. The weather at Lajes was absolutely clear, but wind kept us in Bermuda.

The winds at Lajes sometimes blow fiercely from across the ocean, and this was one of those times. The velocity of the wind at Lajes was more than 110 miles per hour. What made matters worse, the wind was blowing at an angle across the Lajes runway. Trying to land in a crosswind that strong is begging for trouble. In an emergency or war situation, the Hercules would have taken off for Lajes. But this was not an emergency.

We changed our plans. Instead of flying to Lajes and then on to France, Wallick decided to take a different route. He received permission to depart Bermuda and fly nonstop to Moron (pronounced *Mah-rone*) Air Base near Seville, Spain.

Moron Air Base is a combat operations field of the Strategic Air Command, and we could land there, refuel, and remain overnight. We began the long stretch over the Atlantic Ocean, and once again we soared to high altitude. This time, to take advantage of slightly stronger winds from our tail, we climbed to 26,000 feet. At this height the wind blew strongest from the west, which gave us a dividend in speed of 50 miles per hour. On a long flight, that is very welcome.

The skies over the Atlantic were filled with clouds of every size and description. There were stratus clouds far below us, just above the ocean. Cirrus clouds sailed in ghostlike formations miles above us. For a while we flew through cirrus at our own altitude. On the sharp black spinners of the engines, we saw rings of ice. Then we were out of the foglike clouds five miles up, and back into clear air.

Later, cumulus clouds began to build up all around us. Some of them towered to 30,000 and 40,000 feet, well above our altitude. Wallick and Bowman referred to the weather radar-scope as we approached these huge cloud mountains. The weather showed patterns of rain and hail ahead of us. Whenever it looked as though heavy rain showed directly in our path, Wallick maneuvered the Hercules around the area, rather than fly directly through it. Rain heavy enough to show clearly on the scope is usually associated with turbulence. Flying into this kind of turbulence when it can be avoided is both stupid and dangerous. We might fly suddenly into a barrage of hail. And why subject the airplane to possibly violent winds? It would take a storm of immense strength to endanger the powerful structure of the Hercules. But we had passengers in the airplane, and sudden vertical air currents could toss them about wildly. As it was, even dodging the worst of the weather, the Hercules rocked and pitched steadily for about an hour.

An hour after we left the storm area, the sky grew darker. Since we were flying to the east, night fell rapidly. And when finally the skies lost the last strip of red sunset on the horizon, we entered a strange and awesome new world.

In the flight deck we existed in a glow of dark red light. A pilot can observe his instruments under red light, and still not lose the vision he needs to see outside the airplane. White light severely reduces a pilot's night vision. We seemed to be swimming in red. Red glowed from the wide instrument panel, it glowed in straight and curving lines from the electrical and hydraulic control consoles, from the schematic diagrams of the fuel system. Many of the flight instruments gleamed softly in a bluish-green fluorescent glow.

Whenever the crew wanted to examine a particular row of switches or controls, or to study closely their charts, they would unhook a red flashlight. This was part of the aircraft power system, but it threw a stronger red beam. When these special lights were in use, it seemed as though strange globes of red were floating through the flight deck.

Outside the windows and the windshield of the Hercules was a world of incredible lights. So high above the earth that we were beyond the dust, water vapor, and haze of lower altitudes, we could see the stars with brilliant clarity. The Milky Way seemed to be a river of untold billions of gleaming and sparkling lights. There was no moon yet, but the light from the stars was so great that we could see the clouds and the ocean far below us.

Directly above the airplane there shone a red sphere. It was the planet Mars, and it looked like a shining marble hung in the midst of the stars.

Hours later, as we neared the coast of Spain, the moon rose. Now the clouds were revealed brilliantly to us, and we watched the irregular shapes of their shadows on the surface of the dully gleaming ocean. We saw more lights soon afterward, fishing boats at sea, and then brilliant flashes of light from the many lighthouse beacons along the rugged shores of Spain.

We were on our way back to the everyday world. Lights showed more brightly as we passed over towns and cities. Far ahead of us were the alternate flashes of white and green that marked the sprawling airport of the Strategic Air Command base. More and more lights . . . rows of white flashes lead to the runway, then the red lights at the threshold of the runway, and the green lights that run along both sides of the entire runway. We ground to a stop. Major Wallick eased the big airplane off the runway to a taxistrip. In the darkness, we rumbled along between lanes of blue taxiway lights.

Flying at night is a succession of different lights and light signals. A truck with a brilliantly glowing sign at its rear—FOLLOW ME—appeared before us. We followed it to the parking ramp, where a flight line attendant waved two glowing yellow batons for hand signals. Without a word, following the sweeping curves and movements of the yellow batons, Major Wallick parked the airplane, locked the brakes, and shut down the engines that had carried us across the ocean, to Spain.

FRANCE BELOW

From Moron Air Base, the next morning we departed for France. It was an unexciting but wonderful flight, with clouds and mountains providing a change of

scenery as we cruised northward. Most of us had flown
along this same route many times, and we recognized
Bordeaux on the French coast, as the Hercules wheeled
and set its course directly for Evreux-Fauxville Air
Base near Paris.

Once again, we drifted from one electronic highway
to the other. This time, however, the skies were not
empty as they had been in the long flight across the
ocean. We saw the white, cottony vapor trails of jet
fighters and bombers. Many of them were practicing
combat tactics, and in their mock war they wove
strange patterns in the sky. We saw other transports,
and dipped our wings to a Hercules that passed to our
right and below us. The other pilot saw us, and we
watched the Hercules roll slightly from side to side as
he returned the greeting.

Then, for the third time since we left Tennessee, we
were sailing smoothly out of the sky. The long runways
of Evreux-Fauxville appeared far ahead of us. Major
Wallick and his crew would call this base home for the
next three months.

We slid onto the runway without a quiver and rolled
off to the parking area reserved for the rotation squad-
rons from the United States.

The Hercules is a flying airplane, and the 322nd Air
Division has its own proud motto: "You call—We
haul." They do exactly that—anywhere, any time, and
under any conditions.

THE AMAZING HERCULES 9

IN THE MOUNTAINS of India there are crude airstrips hacked by hand out of the steep slopes. When Chinese troops spilled down from their side of the mountainous border to attack India, these airstrips became vital. Only if supplies could be flown into them could the Indian Army try to hold back the enemy. They needed men, guns, ammunition, and other weapons. There wasn't time to bring supplies in by the winding, narrow roads. It had to be done by airlift.

But this is cruel mountain country. The peaks are jagged and sawtoothed. The crude airstrips are so high above sea level that it is always cold. Men and airplanes both need air. The average altitude above sea level is 12,000 feet.

With a heavy load of supplies, many airplanes cannot reach this height. Their propellers whirl at top speed, but the engines gasp for air. Their power is 40 per cent of maximum, if that much. The controls are sloppy. The airplane responds poorly and mushes in flight. It is deadly flying—and more than one of these fields is littered with the wreckage of crashed airplanes.

Landing in the thin air is a brutal business. Crews are

pounded in their seats and hurled against their restraining straps.

The strips are rough; many are bumpy and strewn with rocks. Some are extremely short. There is one, at 14,000 feet, that is especially bad. Few pilots dare to land there because it is not more than 2,000 feet long. This is considered short at sea level, where the air is dense, even for a small airplane.

The field is so high that if a man performs any strenuous work he may collapse. Unless he has an oxygen system with him and uses an oxygen mask he will slump into unconsciousness.

Only one airplane can operate from this strip while carrying a cargo load, and that is the Lockheed C-130 Hercules. This was the airplane sent by the 322nd Air Division to assist the Indians.

Let us watch as a Hercules takes off from this airstrip nearly three miles high.

The pilot taxies to the last available inch of runway. The engines spin at nearly 14,000 revolutions per minute. In the thin air the propellers flash brightly. The brakes are on and locked. Everything is running at maximum power. Then the pilot demands full thrust from his propellers. The great blades change their pitch, shift their position. Now they bite with voracious gulps into the air.

The Hercules shakes through every fiber. It vibrates and rocks as if it were straining to break free of its brakes. The pilot makes one last check of the airplane. He turns and nods to the copilot, and chops the brakes free.

The Hercules bolts forward. Propellers howling, the airplane punches down the strip and claws desperately for speed. There is nothing like a go-no-go operation here; there is no stopping at the end of the field, to retry a takeoff. If the airplane runs out of airstrip and it still isn't flying, why, you can erase one airplane and her crew off the books. It is as simple and as harsh as that.

The pilot holds the rocking, bucking Hercules on the ground until the last possible moment. He needs every last fraction of speed those engines can give to him. Nothing is more precious that speed to shape the airflow past the wings, to slam into the flaps, to create the magic of lift. There is no time for second thoughts.

Suddenly, the pitifully short runway is gone. There is nothing left now except huge boulders and a hill. The pilot has no choice; he hauls back on the control yoke.

It is not a smooth takeoff. There is very little that is coordinated about it. Just haul back on the yoke, and pray that the wings are grabbing air, because there is a jagged ridge directly ahead.

The pilot calls on all his skill and experience. Flying with razor precision in the thin air, he lifts the Hercules off the ground. The instant the control yoke comes back, the flight engineer hits the gear switch. He wastes no time in cutting down the drag of the extended wheels. Anything that helps to build up speed is vital.

The Hercules heaves itself from the strip. With scant feet to spare it clears a jump just beyond the end of the strip. Almost at once the pilot drops the nose back to level flight. The airplane skims the surface without gaining altitude.

The pilot has only a limited distance, and very little time, to build up the speed he needs. He has passed the first test—getting into the air. Now he must clear a mountain.

The jagged wall rushes closer. The airspeed builds up slowly in the thin air. The pilot must fly straight ahead. Banking the wings would mean a loss of speed, and he cannot afford to do that.

He flies directly at the mountain. No one even feels or notices that the Hercules is trembling in the air currents sweeping across the ridges. Only two things matter now, the mountain, and the needle on the airspeed indicator dial.

Abruptly the mountain is beginning to fill the sky. It seems to rush upon the Hercules. This is a good sign; it means the airplane is accelerating rapidly. The pilot judges distance and speed with care; if he does not judge properly, the airplane will smash against that unyielding rock.

The control yoke comes back and the nose lifts. In a great soaring rush the big airplane bursts into the sky. The propellers flash in the sun, their sound booming back and forth between the mountain walls.

Higher and higher—the jagged ramparts are close now. The ridges are irregular, and the Hercules must be flown with precision. There is a gap in those walls no more than 500 feet wide. But it is wide enough, and the Hercules flashes through.

A second and higher mountain lies directly ahead. But there will be no attempt to climb this peak. Now there is enough speed, the grip of the wings on the air is solid and secure. The control yoke comes over to the right and the pilot's foot presses down on the right rudder pedal. The Hercules wheels around in a sweeping bank. It wheels through the sanctuary of air.

Metal flashes over rock, but it is several hundred feet below. The mountain slides by to the left, far beyond the wing.

The men in the flight deck relax. Ahead of the Hercules is a long and deep valley. Gravity is a friend now, and the pilot drops the nose slightly. Speed builds with a rush. Minutes later the Hercules is nearly 30,000 feet high, master once again of the mountains of this world.

This takeoff is not a one-time performance. It has been done many times, and with a perfect safety record.

The test of any airplane really begins once it is in the hands of the people who use it on a day-to-day basis. Gone is the special attention of the most skillful technicians. The airplane must deliver its promise, or it is a failure. The takeoff from India is a perfect example. No test pilot in his right mind would ever have attempted such a critical maneuver as part of a "prove it" campaign.

In a 1960 combat exercise, known as Banyan Tree II, a fleet of C-130B Hercules gave a dramatic demonstration of power when waves of Hercules transports thundered over Panama. More than a thousand fighting men spilled out of the airplanes to drop earthward beneath their parachutes.

Six nations from South America participated with TAC in the combat maneuvers. The paratroopers from the United States were rushed 2,000 miles nonstop before they reached the drop zone. Other Hercules' came close behind. Each of these airplanes dropped up to 38,000 pounds of equipment and weapons by parachute.

Banyan Tree II and other maneuvers involved as much as 70,000 men in realistic combat simulations. They all proved the versatility of the Hercules to meet any situation, any time, any place.

Despite its success, TAC wanted still more performance from its C-130B assault transports. The 463rd Troop Carrier Wing at Sewart AFB received an assignment that gave special meaning to the term assault transport. The Air Force wanted true STOL (Short Takeoff and Landing) performance.

The Hercules flew to an abandoned strip in an isolated forest area. The strip hadn't been used for years, and had fallen apart as weeds and heavy brush chewed the runway into such a mess that jeeps had to crawl slowly over its surface.

The Hercules' pilots were told that they were to land and take off in a distance of 1,500 feet. Not one foot more.

This is not difficult if the airplane is stripped to light weight. But these airplanes were not stripped. They pounded and slammed down onto the rugged strip weighing 120,000 pounds. The big transports thundered in and out of the tiny strip as though this was the normal way to fly.

But could the airplane operate from the same strip at a weight of 135,000 pounds?

Lockheed engineers worked day and night, and came up with changes to the airplane. The flaps came down lower from the wings than they had before. They operated faster too. The engineers modified the giant rudder, improved the aileron control slightly. And then, they added a 22-foot diameter drag parachute to the tail.

When the pilots learned that they were to release the parachute in the air, they didn't believe it. But it was true. The parachute would act as a tremendous brake on the airplane.

Weighing 135,000 pounds, the Hercules slammed into the strip, again and again. When the tests were over, the Hercules had again exceeded all expectations. With its full weight the STOL C-130B could wham into a strip only 1,400 feet long. It could dump its cargo, load on new cargo or wounded, and be off the strip within minutes of touching down.

SOUTH VIETNAM

About 80 miles southwest of Saigon there is a short airstrip used by Japanese fighters in World War II. It is in the middle of thick jungle, and is exactly 2,900 feet long. When a group of Marine Corps Hercules' arrived at the strip, they were the first airplanes in the area for more than fifteen years. During that time the strip had been at the mercy of storms and jungle growth.

If a pilot took off in one direction from the strip, he quickly found himself staring at trees at least 90 feet high. But the pilots preferred this course, even if the wind wasn't from the right direction for takeoff. Going the other way meant flying over a small town, and Communist guerrillas there and in the surrounding jungle were waiting to pour bullets and shells into the American airplanes.

The Marines considered the alternative and figured that the trees, at least, wouldn't shoot back. Then men on the strip used to watch the tops of the trees bend and sway from the rush of air as the transports boomed into the sky.

The Marine operation with the Hercules' in South Vietnam was known as Operation X-Ray. There were eleven airplanes in all. They operated out of Cubi Point in the Philippines, and flew missions directly to the abandoned airstrip.

The Marine Hercules' roared out of the Philippines in a steady procession. Each plane made at least one and sometimes two complete round trips a day. They hauled heavily-armed fighting men into the jungle. They hauled jeeps, trucks, ammunition, food, and other combat gear and supplies.

Each time they flew, they took off with 28,000 pounds of cargo and 36,000 pounds of fuel in their wing tanks. This enabled them to leave the Philippines and climb to 26,000 feet, cruise to the Saigon area, make a jet penetration and land, then, without refueling, to return to Cubi Point.

A Hercules sails past the snow-covered peak of Mount Fujiyama, Japan. (*U.S. Air Force*)

Time on the ground: no more than 15 minutes maximum per airplane.

Then, the rains started. Every day the skies poured cascades of water onto the airstrip. The battering by the airplanes, and the torrents of water ripped and tore at the old concrete strip.

Water collected in great pools, and the Hercules splashed through it and onto broken concrete. On one occasion a great chunk of concrete damaged a Hercules. This was the first incident of its kind—the first damage received by any of the transports in the jungle operation.

But the Hercules isn't a flying boat, and water at 100 miles per hour can be dangerous. The airplane pounded into the deep pools; the water smashed back with jackhammer pressure and twisted metal doors out of shape.

One Hercules damaged its nose gear so badly that it failed to lower into position for landing. The pilot made an emergency landing, holding the airplane on its main gear, and the nose high. Finally, the nose dropped, and the jagged concrete mangled the bottom of the nose and the belly.

The Marines swarmed forward and jacked up the nose. They heaved mightily and forced the damaged metal out of the way. Then they lowered the nose gear and locked it into place. Minutes later, the airplane took off and roared back to the Philippines.

The Marine mechanics worked all night on the

damaged Hercules. The next morning it was back on the regular scheduled runs of the airlift.

Many of the stories about the Hercules in South Vietnam, India, and other parts of the world where nations are torn by war must wait to be told. Secrecy is still necessary to conceal the details of operations even more astounding than those we have told.

But for the record, the Hercules has demonstrated by brilliant performance its role as a battle-scarred and battle-proven assault transport.

THE TWO-EDGED SWORD   10

SWORDS ARE made with two cutting edges. One may be used for purposes of war. The other can serve the purposes of peace, for it can be used as a tool for all manner of needs. It can be used to help rather than to kill.

The Hercules has proved to be a weapon with two cutting edges. If this airplane had never fulfilled a single military mission, it would still be worth its cost a thousand times over.

The Hercules has carried food, medicine, doctors, relief supplies, mobile hospitals, and construction equipment. It has transported the sick and the maimed, and refugees fleeing from disasters. Many of these missions do not make headlines. But it is often the everyday role of an airplane that has the greatest meaning.

On February 29, 1960, an earthquake shattered the Moroccan city of Agadir. Before the dust settled to the ground, ten thousand people were dead. Many of the survivors were badly injured. Almost the entire city was homeless. In the ensuing hours, rats fled their warrens and ran among the dead and the wounded. The nightmare of the plague hung over Agadir.

A cry for help went out from the Moroccan people. The United States responded immediately. We sent aid from our naval forces in the Mediterranean and from our airbases in Africa.

The 332nd Air Division in France received its orders to move out, not with fighting men or weapons, but with help for Agadir. Fifty-two transports roared into the air. Of these, four out of every five were the high-winged Hercules. Their high speed and long range made them the vanguard of the aerial bridge to Agadir.

Six hundred tons of supplies, as well as five hundred skilled engineers, doctors, and technicians crossed that bridge. Americans in Air Force, Army, and Navy uniforms worked day and night to save lives. They tended the wounded, helped bury the dead, and provided food, clothing and shelter for the living. They clothed and took care of thirty thousand people.

The Hercules' transports thundered steadily into the Agadir area. They rolled bulldozers off their ramps so that Army engineers could clear the rubble-choked streets. When the Hercules' took off, they were filled with the wounded who had to be rushed to hospitals, many miles away.

Four months after the Agadir operation, violence exploded in the Congo. The United Nations decided to commit troops and weapons to the area to hold down the violence and the bloodshed. On July 14, 1960, the 322nd Air Division at Evreux-Fauxville Air Base in France received orders to supply the airlift.

The next morning the Hercules' were in the air. For ten days they flew almost constantly. In the initial phase of the emergency airlift, the Hercules' flew five thousand heavily armed U.N. soldiers to the Congo.

They also carried a million pounds of food to starving people in the area.

This was only the beginning. Aboard the Hercules transports in the weeks following were men from Tunisia, Morocco, Ghana, Sweden, Guinea, Ethiopia, Liberia, Ireland, Mali, Sudan, India, United Arab Republic, Canada, Pakistan, Nigeria, and Australia. In the first five months of the airlift, planes of the Military Air Transport Service (MATS) provided assistance. Together, the 322nd and MATS carried sixteen thousand soldiers and nearly six million pounds of supplies into the Congo. Returning aircraft carried refugees and injured out of the area.

The Hercules' transports of the 322nd Air Division turned in an astounding record of performance. In more than six hundred missions to the Congo (averaging 3,500 miles per mission), they had to fly to many remote airfields. They landed the airplanes down on grass and dirt fields (*not* airports). They went just about anywhere and everywhere.

And they had a perfect safety record!

By July 1962, two years after the start of the Congo

Flood-relief supplies destined for Somalia villages are loaded aboard a C-130A of the 322nd Air Division, at Mogadiscio, Somalia. (*U.S. Air Force*)

airlift, nearly one thousand three hundred separate mission flights, the transports had carried fifty-seven thousand seven hundred and fourteen people, as well as 8,665 tons of cargo.

They did this in a total of thirty-three thousand hours of flying without a single flying accident. They did this over some of the most formidable and dangerous terrain on earth. Navigation facilities were nonexistent. Maintenance operations resembled those of an isolated outfit of World War II with nothing but the most primitive facilities. An ingenious flight engineer had to change an engine, but lacked the equipment to do the job. He roared into a small town in a jeep, rented an auto wrecker for five dollars, and raced back to the airplane. The crew used the ancient wrecker as a hoist and sling, and changed the engine.

An Air Force maintenance officer with the Hercules force told the author:

"We had plenty of systems failures in the C-130's in that operation, but we had fewer in the '130 than we did in the other cargo planes. And when the other planes had a system failure—that was it. The crew had to wait on the ground for parts and mechanics before they could get moving.

"But we never put a Hercules out of commission in the bush when something failed. That machine has so many backup systems that when something went haywire, the crew could just shut it down, use the backup, and continue right along with their mission."

There are hundreds of isolated Hercules flights known as "Helping Hand Missions" that never made newspaper copy. A boy is critically ill and must be moved swiftly to a distant hospital. A patient in an iron lung must be transferred to a hospital. These are normal missions for the Hercules.

And then, there are the tragic mass disasters. In October 1960 two cyclones smashed across East Pakistan. Then huge tidal waves pounded the shorelines. When the storms had passed, twelve thousand people were dead, many thousands missing, and one hundred thousand homeless.

Six Hercules of the 322nd Air Division sped more than 6,000 miles to bring relief to the suffering country. They carried 100,000 pounds of blankets; 6,250 pounds of sulfa drugs; 200 pounds of antimalaria tablets; 6,486 pounds of multivitamin tablets; and 42,000 pounds of other supplies.

Hercules transports, in November 1961, brought supplies to flood-stricken areas of Kenya and Somalia. Three months later, fifteen Hercules roared into the flooded regions near Hamburg, Germany, with more than 230,000 pounds of clothing and blankets when the German Red Cross appealed for help. The first group of Hercules' was in the air only two hours after the appeal was received.

In September 1962, an earthquake shattered northwestern Iran. An area as large as Massachusetts and Connecticut was devastated. Ten thousand people were killed outright, ten thousand were injured and twenty-five thousand made homeless. Food and water supplies were destroyed and medical care was nonexistent. It was believed to be the greatest calamity in the 2,500-year history of Iran.

Twenty-eight Hercules of the 322nd Air Division sped to Iran. In the first sixty-eight hours of the airlift they carried more than a million pounds of supplies to the stricken area. They brought in 1,000 tents; 10,000 blankets; a complete field hospital with 128 beds, two hundred doctors, nurses and medical technicians; and many tons of food and water.

KALEIDOSCOPE 11

IN 1957 THE AIR FORCE completed its extensive tests of the ski-equipped C-130D Hercules. As quickly as Lockheed could prepare the skis, a force of Hercules' was ordered to carry out the job of carrying men and material to the DEW (Distant Early Warning) line construction sites. Weighing 124,000 pounds, the airplanes pounded across snow and ice and climbed into the air with only 2,100 feet of takeoff run. Using special techniques developed in the tests, the pilots could slide to a stop after a landing distance of only 1,200 feet.

This was unprecedented for snow-and-ice operations.

Twelve Hercules' of the 314th Troop Carrier Wing moved in a group to Sondestrom airbase in southern Greenland. For the next six months they operated on an almost ceaseless schedule. As many as ten airplanes were in the air at one time, flying to different points on the icecap. The men started flying at four A.M. and worked straight through the long hours of daylight. The need for equipment was critical.

161

Skis and wheels enable a C-130D to bring supplies to the isolated and snowbound DEW East radar station in Greenland. (*Federal Electric Corporation*)

During these six months, the twelve C-130D transports landed and took off from the icecap more than 2,500 times. The conditions under which they flew were extremely difficult. The icecap itself is at an elevation of 10,000 feet. In that thin air, the Hercules operated with a weight of 62 tons. The huge skis formed air drag to hold down the airplane's performance. At sea level this would not have mattered much—two miles high it was most important. The Hercules' operated in snow from four to ten feet deep. The temperature often fell to 40° below zero.

Every day that the weather permitted (no flying in blizzards), the crews were in the air. The ice storms were the worst hazard. They could coat an airplane with many tons of ice. This overloaded the planes and destroyed the flow of air and lift across the wings. There were magnetic and solar storms that could not be seen. They raged hundreds of miles high and blacked out all radio communications. The airplanes had to remain in the ice, their instruments and radio equipment useless.

There were also whiteouts when the pilot had no ground reference of any kind. Everything was white. It was like flying around in the inside of a milk bottle. When whiteouts occurred the crew was cut off completely from the world. The pilot flew on instruments, and even landed by instruments.

At the end of the six-months mission in 1959, the Hercules crews had flown a total of three thousand hours with the twelve airplanes. They had hauled 26,-000,000 pounds of cargo to all the radar sites. And they completed the backbreaking task nine days ahead of schedule.

In 1960 the Hercules' came back to Greenland to finish the two-year job. This time they carried 23,-000,000 pounds of equipment. All told, the Hercules' carried nearly 25,000 tons of supplies, and thousands of passengers.

The United States Navy then ordered ski-equipped

Hercules' transports for use in Antarctica. The Navy airplanes were then known as the C-130BL; today they are called the LC-130F.

But until delivery could be made, the Navy borrowed some Air Force ski-Hercules' and their crews for Operation Deep Freeze (1960). The Hercules' transports left the top of the world and began the long journey to Antarctica at the opposite side of the planet.

AT THE BOTTOM OF THE WORLD

At the South Pole (elevation: 10,000 feet), there are few dust particles or smoke. The air is unbelievably

This Air Force C-130D has just brought supplies to Antarctica. When the picture was taken the temperature had dropped to 50 degrees below zero. (*U.S. Navy*)

Gleaming in the brilliant sun at the bottom of the world—an
Air Force C-130D roars over Navy installations in Antarctica.
(*U.S. Navy*)

clear. It is bitter cold. The stars seem at least twice as bright as those you see from the United States. It is like looking upon a vast field of distant stars.

Lockheed Engineer Bill Smith has described the great aurora of the southern polar skies. "In front and to the side of the airplane soared great shimmering curtains of color—orange, yellow, red—like a gossamer curtain that danced and moved. Suddenly, it seemed as though the Hercules was going to fly straight into the great sheets of color. The next minute they had shifted and were far to the side of the airplane."

In the words of Rear Admiral David M. Tyree, Commander of the United States Support Force for Antarctica: "Antarctica is the coldest, highest, windiest continent on earth. At the same time, it is dramatically and fantastically one of the most beautiful. Mountain ranges rising high along the coast show constantly changing colors in the summer sun. The interior of the continent is a great ice plateau which rises as high as fourteen thousand feet. Rivers of ice flow down the valleys leading to the coast producing innumerable glaciers. Temperatures range from a record winter low of minus 110° at the Pole Station to a few degrees above freezing occasionally at McMurdo and more frequently at Hallett in the summer. Vicious Antarctic blizzards rise with sudden fury . . .

"It is also the unforgiving continent. Usually, the Antarctic lets you make only one mistake—this can be your last."

The Hercules' were sent to Antarctica to help re-
supply the Antarctic stations, and Admiral Tyree pre-
dicted that they would cut in half the cost of operations
in Antarctica and create an aerial supply line directly
to the South Pole itself. For Deep Freeze '60, Lieutenant Colonel Wilbur Turk led seven C-130D Hercules' on a 13,850-mile flight to Antarctica. The Air
Force called the mission Operation Ice Flow.

As the first Hercules roared onto the frozen runway
near McMurdo Sound, the horizon vanished. Blinding
white dazzled the eye. The navigators stayed glued to
their radar sets, and directed the pilots to the surface.

For their first mission, the Hercules' were to take
400 tons of supplies from McMurdo Sound to the
South Pole (850 miles away) and to Marie Byrd Land
(950 miles). The job had to be done before the long
winter completely isolated the stations.

The seven C-130D Hercules' made 58 supply runs.
In twelve days they had carried four hundred tons of
supplies to the scientific outpost. And they had completed the assignment ten days ahead of schedule. This
despite winds that abruptly changed course and
screeched with explosive force across the ice runways.
One huge transport even slid sideways down the ice.

Frederick G. Vosburgh of the National Geographic
Society summed up the missions: "To those of us who
rode to the Pole in the big, squat Lockheed Hercules',
it was plain as the icicles on a polar scientist's beard
that these jet-turbine propeller-driven planes will lop

years off the time required for the exploration and mapping of Antarctica. With the Ski-130's available for carrying aviation gasoline in bulk, Antarctic personnel can make the Pole a big fuel depot for trail support, rescue, and photomapping planes. By airlifting diesel oil and snow vehicles, they can also make it a jumping-off place for scientific transverse parties. Instead of a precarious outpost of science, Admundsen-Scott (the Pole Station) will have become a major advance base for exploration on the other side of the pole."

In 1961 the Navy moved in its new ski-Hercules planes, operating with Squadron VX-6.

For Deep Freeze '61, the Hercules' flew 1,800 tons of supplies to the remote sites. This was four and a half times the tonnage of the previous year. The VX-6 Squadron exceeded all their missions and requirements. In four days the three Hercules' flew twenty missions. On one trip a Hercules flew 3,024 miles across the continent at 24,000 feet, unloaded passengers and cargo at a rough airstrip in the Walker Mountains, and returned to its base. The complete round trip was flown in eleven hours, a record in the history of Antarctic transportation.

A Hercules can release an entire cargo in five minutes, as in top photo, by taxiing around the site at slow speed in a wide circle while crewmen slide cargo down ramp. At Antarctica (below) the airplane must sometimes land amid howling winds and blowing snow. (*U.S. Navy*)

In April of 1961 Antarctica was closed to all flying. This was the beginning of the seven-month period when the ice continent is isolated from the outside world. But a Russian scientist became critically ill. Despite the danger, a Navy Hercules, on April 9, sped to Byrd Station, picked up the scientist, and flew him to a hospital in New Zealand.

The mercy flight of Commander Newcomer and his crew was one of the greatest flights of Antarctic exploration. In the face of diminishing daylight and increasingly vicious and frequent winter storms they breached the curtain of Antarctica's winter isolation for the first time. A new era in Antarctic exploration had begun.

KALEIDOSCOPE

It would be impossible to record in detail all the missions and accomplishments of the Hercules. There are now eighteen versions of the transport, and more are being planned.

The Seeing Eye Hercules (RC-130A), for example,

Hercules delivers scientific supplies (top) to Antarctic station. In an emergency mission (below) Hercules flew to McMurdo Sound after permanent Antarctic night had set in, to pick up a critically-ill scientist. Here, crewmen are pre-heating Hercules interior before takeoff. (*U.S. Navy*) carries photographic, electronic, and computer equipment. A special force of these airplanes is now engaged in the greatest aerial survey and map-making mission in history. Research carried out by the RC-130A proved that Iceland is actually six hundred feet from where it now appears on maps. Cuba is 1,200 feet out of position, and the Cuban coast line curves differently than our maps show. Grand Bahama Island is some 32,000 feet out of alignment.

The importance of this mission cannot be underestimated. For example, one of the tracking stations of our deep-space network was "way out of its believed position." Now that its exact location is known, the tracking radar can work with much greater accuracy.

The Hercules is used to test new parachute designs and equipment. The Mercury space capsule was heaved from Hercules transports during the early parachute and drop tests. They are now being used to test the parachute system of the two-man Gemini.

Special models of the C-130 track and record data from missiles and space vehicles fired from Cape Kennedy. In the Pacific, Hercules' do the same job for shots made from the Pacific Missile Range launching site at Vandenberg Air Force Base.

The JC-130B Hercules is used in air-sea rescue operations. This airplane can snatch men, or objects as heavy as 6,000 pounds, from heavy seas, snow, or rugged terrain without touching the surface. It is equipped with CARTS—C-130B Aerial Retrieval and Transport System.

Like a ghost out of the silver-grey sky, an Air Force C-130D ski-equipped Hercules slides in for an icy landing at Byrd Station, Antarctica. (*U.S. Navy*)

A nylon line released by a man in a raft is attached to a helium-filled balloon. This brings the balloon to a height of 250 feet. The man wears a harness, and the nylon line is attached to securing rings in the harness. (If the man in the liferaft does not have this equipment, the Hercules drops it to him by parachute.)

With the balloon holding up the line, the Hercules comes overhead at 150 miles per hour. It trails a snare loop in an outrigger attachment. The snare captures the nylon line and hauls the man into the air. The crew then operates a power winch and brings the man safely into the airplane.

A CARTS-equipped Hercules can seek, save, and recover space capsules, nose cones, and, above all, men. One Hercules on a single flight can pick up twenty-two men from the ocean. The system has worked in hundreds of operations.

It's also worked in spectacular air-snatches of capsules returning from orbit. The Air Force has used the Hercules for years to recover Discoverer capsules that orbited the earth at 18,000 miles per hour. After reentry, the capsules release a parachute and float earthward. Older C-119 planes could make only two or three passes to capture the chute. The speed, maneuverability, and high-altitude operation of the Hercules enable it to make at least seven passes. And if the Hercules misses the capsule in the air, it can snatch it from the sea.

There is still another role played by the Hercules in snatch operations. Using a new technique, a small team of men uses any cleared area quickly to set up a

In the first joint exercises for American and Japanese paratroopers, a Japanese trooper jumps from the rear ramp of a United States Air Force Hercules. (*Lockheed-Georgia*)

A JC-130B modified to recover returning space capsules—as capsules enter the atmosphere, small parachutes open to slow down their descent, while the Hercules races in swiftly to snare them in its special trapeze-boom rig. (*Lockheed-Georgia*)

cable-snatch system. They stretch a cable across the ground and run it to drums placed in water.

The airplane flies over the field at low speed, just a few feet over the ground. The heavy cargo pallet (trucks, tanks, jeeps, equipment) in the fuselage trails a long hook. As the Hercules rumbles by in the air, the hook grabs the cable. The cable draws taut, and the cargo pallet is whisked right out of the airplane. The speeding cargo pallet pulls on the cable, and the cable in turn pulls the drums in the water. The drag of the water provides a slow deceleration. There is no damage to the cargo.

One crew taped a raw egg to the radiator of a jeep on a snatch pallet. When the jeep bounced to a stop there wasn't a crack on the egg.

The cargo pallet system has proved so successful that there is now a people pallet. As many as fifteen men are placed in a special pallet which has seats built to take shocks and decelerations. In the same way that the cargo is snatched from the Hercules, the people pallets are whisked out of the airplane. The men hit the ground in the pallet, slide along for a few seconds, and come to a stop. They step out ready to fight.

A unique space-support mission for the Hercules has turned it into a flying firehouse. Out in the California desert, there are many broad and flat dry lake beds. These are assigned as emergency landing fields to the X-15 rocket research airplane. Sometimes the X-15 must land many miles from the nearest installation in an area surrounded by high mountains. If there is a mechanical failure, the X-15 might catch fire, and the pilot be trapped.

On one occasion the X-15 did land on a dry lake

bed, and the pilot reported danger of fire. As the X-15 slid down the dusty surface, a Hercules screamed down a mountain slope and landed on the same lake bed. As it neared the research airplane, the cargo ramp came down. The Hercules pilot reversed the propellers and applied his brakes. The airplane came to a sudden stop in billowing clouds of dust.

Out of the back end of the Hercules, sirens screaming and red lights flashing, came a fire truck. With an emergency crash crew, carrying water and chemicals, it roared over to the X-15. The crew opened the escape doors, pulled the pilot free, and poured foam onto the airplane. There was no fire—yet, and the crew made sure there would be none at all.

THE BIG E

On April 6, 1962, the first of a new breed of Hercules' —the C-130E—went on operational duty with the Military Air Transport Service (MATS).

The first step in modernizing our nation's airlift capacity had been the Hercules itself. Then came the new C-130E, which General Curtis E. LeMay called "the second stage of . . . airlift modernization."

The E model looks almost exactly like its C-130B predecessor, with one noticeable difference. Beneath each wing is a giant fuel tank. With these new tanks, plus the wet wing, the C-130E has a fuel capacity of

GC-130 (top) is a missile launcher. It is shown with four Q-2C drone missiles that are launched three to four miles high. The Military Air Transport Service (MATS) operates different versions of the Hercules, including their own C-130B Weatherbird model (below) used for global weather reporting. (*Lockheed-Georgia*)

nearly 10,000 gallons. It is an outstanding strategic transport.

Carrying 24,000 pounds of cargo (any type), the C-130E can fly nonstop for a distance of 4,600 miles. In combat situations the C-130E model can cross the Atlantic with a payload of 34,000 pounds at a speed of six miles a minute. Twelve hours after leaving the United States, fighting men can be at their European destination. Making only one stop to refuel, the Big E can leap the Pacific at the same 360-mile-per-hour speed.

Without any additional power over the C-130B model, the Big E lifts from the ground with a gross weight of 155,000 pounds. It can fly, with reduced cargo, 5,000 miles nonstop and then land on rough and unimproved surface less than 3,000 feet in length.

The big turbojets are faster than the E, but they cannot carry the bulky cargo, and they are almost helpless when it comes to landing on rough surfaces. They must have enormous stretches of concrete to land safely.

What about maximum payload of the Big E? That is perhaps the most astonishing thing about the latest Hercules—it can carry a cargo load of 56,000 pounds.

The new C-130E model Hercules can race over 4,000 miles nonstop with a heavy load and "dump in" to a rough, unimproved dirt strip. (*Lockheed-Georgia*)

In closing . . .

With the Big E, the United States gained tremendous flexibility in aerial operations. The Hercules can fly from fields as short as 1,400 feet in STOL combat operations and leap from one continent to another, carrying heavy cargo and personnel payloads not just for the Tactical Air Command, or Strike Command, or for the Navy. For the Hercules in its different models also flies with the Marines and the Coast Guard, and carries out a variety of missions that number into the hundreds.

But the most important judgment of any transport airplane must be that of the man who does not fly. This is the man on the firing line, who is not a pilot, but who willingly entrusts his life to the Hercules to bring him to battle.

When a grizzled master sergeant first saw the Hercules, he walked around the big airplane with a mixture of open suspicion and an attitude of "What the devil is this thing?"

Months later he had made two dozen jumps from the Hercules and had made several assault landings. With this experience, he could say what the Hercules means to him as a soldier:

"When you fight the kind of guerrilla and jungle wars they're fighting today, you need an airplane that keeps two thousand men going and shooting.

"Those fighters are great, but they can't come down

below the treetops in the jungle to see what's going on.

"The Hercules may not carry any guns herself, but she's the greatest weapon we've had in many years."

And nothing finer could be said about an airplane— specially one with two cutting edges: one for war and one for peace.

ABOUT THE AUTHOR:

The author of more than forty books on flying, aviation, aerospace science, rockets missiles and nuclear
science, Martin Caidin is regarded as one of the outstanding authorities on these subjects.

As a pilot he has flown his own plane throughout the
United States, and has flown a variety of civilian and
military aircraft. He is the only civilian ever to fly with
the famed Thunderbirds. He flew with them in 1960 for
six weeks, living as a member of the team, while he was
working on his book *Thunderbirds!*, which the Avia-
tion/Space Writers Association awarded the James J.
Strebig Memorial Trophy. It was the second time
Martin Caidin had received this coveted award.

His other books for young people include *By Apollo
to the Moon, Aviation and Space Medicine: Man Con-
quers the Vertical Frontier,* written in collaboration
with his wife, Grace, and *Test Pilot.*

Mr. and Mrs. Caidin live in Plainview, New York,
with their two daughters, Jamie and Pamela.